Y0-CBW-678

Popular Canadian Curriculum Series

English • Math • Science • Social Studies

Grades

5•6

Credits

Photo (Cover "children" Sergey Novikov/123RF.com)

Copyright © 2018 Popular Book Company (Canada) Limited

SummerSmart is a registered trademark of Popular Book Company (Canada) Limited, used under licence.

All rights reserved. No part of this publication may be reproduced, stored in a retrieval system, or transmitted in any form or by any means, electronic, mechanical, photocopying, recording or otherwise, without the prior written permission of the Publisher, Popular Book Company (Canada) Limited.

Printed in China

 ISBN: 978-1-77149-281-2

Contents

Grades 5–6

Week

Week

Dear Parent:

While all work and no play makes Jack a dull boy, all play and no work would probably make Jack forget most of what he has learned, which is why it is necessary to schedule regular practice in the long summer vacation to help your child consolidate what he or she has learned.

This is where Canadian Curriculum SummerSmart can help.

Canadian Curriculum SummerSmart provides practice for your child to review the essentials taught in the previous academic year and prepares him or her for the grade ahead with confidence. The series is organized in an easy-to-use format: each title is made up of eight weeks (units) of work so your child can complete one unit each week during the summer vacation. The units are comprised of practice in English, Math, Science, and Social Studies. Engaging Arts and Crafts activities, as well as Comics and Fun Places to Go in Summer, are also included for added fun.

Your child will be delighted to have Canadian Curriculum SummerSmart as his or her summer learning buddy.

Your Partner in Education,
Popular Book Company (Canada) Limited

English

- distinguish facts from opinions
- find definitions of words using context clues
- write interview questions
- find homophones

Mathematics

- measure perimeters and angles
- read a number line
- write equivalent fractions
- solve word problems

Science

- name energy sources
- identify renewable and non-renewable energy sources

Social Studies

- identify the symbols of Canada

J. K. Rowling *Is "Rowling" in Magic*

Week 1

English

A. Read the passage.

Joanne Kathleen Rowling, author of the immensely popular Harry Potter book series, went from an ordinary existence to stardom virtually overnight. The fame bestowed upon Joanne was beyond her wildest dreams.

Joanne actually came up with the idea for the series in 1990, while sitting on a train in England. Rowling spent the next six years completing the first novel and plotting out the themes of the remaining six books. As a single parent with little money, Joanne would escape her dismal dwelling, with her daughter in a baby stroller, and head to a café to write about the Wizard and the "Muggle" worlds.

The first book of the fantasy series, *Harry Potter and the Philosopher's Stone,* was published in 1997. It was a smashing success. Since then, J. K. Rowling has produced a sequel nearly every year, with each subsequent book having even darker undertones. However, each story does have the underlying themes of friendship, good conquering evil, and individuality.

J. K. Rowling is enjoying the success of her now established writings. Her books are published in numerous countries around the world and have been translated into 65 different languages. Also, film versions have earned rave reviews and the consumer industry has taken off with an endless list of Harry Potter paraphernalia. Beyond the books, films, and product lines, this fantasy book series has changed the shape of literature and has transcended the divisions of age.

B. Determine whether the following statements are facts or opinions. Write the letters.

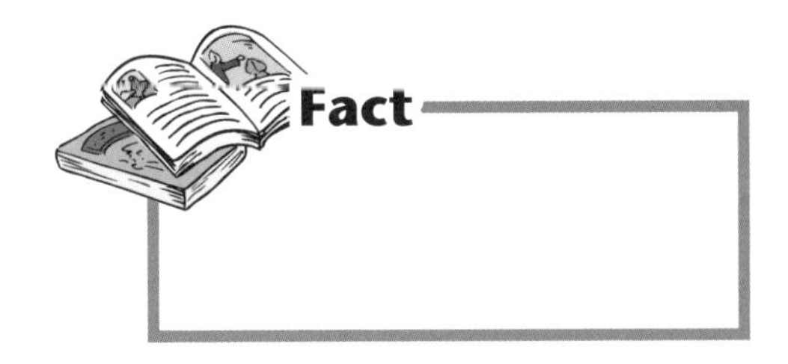

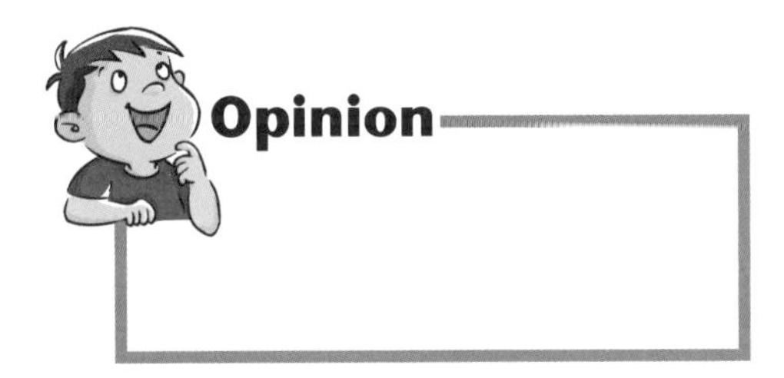

(A) The Harry Potter series is about the Wizard and the "Muggle" worlds.

(B) J. K. Rowling went from an ordinary existence to stardom overnight.

(C) *Harry Potter and the Philosopher's Stone* was published in 1997.

(D) The book was a smashing success.

(E) J. K. Rowling came up with the idea for the series in 1990.

(F) In the beginning, J. K. Rowling often wrote in a café.

C. Find these words in the passage and use context clues* to determine their meanings.

* *When reading an unfamiliar word, it is helpful to use the sentence that the word is in to try to understand its meaning. This is called a context clue.*

1. immensely ____________________
2. bestowed ____________________
3. dismal ____________________
4. paraphernalia ____________________
5. transcended ____________________

Check with a dictionary when you have finished.

D. Complete the sentences with the given nouns. Make the nouns plural before using them.

dormitory	dream	review	
class	alley	life	bench
industry	werewolf	country	

1. At first, Harry thought ______________ were killing the unicorns.
2. The Dursleys' ______________ changed when Harry was placed on their doorstep.
3. The spectators sit on ______________ to watch a Quidditch match.
4. At night, the Hogwarts students sleep in their ______________ .
5. There are many ______________ , but there is only one Diagon Alley.
6. Of all the ______________ that Harry takes, he dislikes Professor Snape's the most.
7. J. K. Rowling cannot believe that her publishing ______________ came true.
8. The film, book, and consumer ______________ are reaping the benefits of J. K. Rowling's masterpiece.
9. The Harry Potter stories are read by children in different ______________ all over the world.
10. The film versions of the Harry Potter novels have also earned rave ______________ .

E. You have just been asked to interview J. K. Rowling. Use "How" and the "5 W's of writing" to compose your questions.

1. How ______________________
2. Who ______________________
3. What ______________________
4. Where ______________________
5. When ______________________
6. Why ______________________

F. Write the homophone of each word.

1. grown ________ 2. allowed ________
3. threw ________ 4. stair ________
5. course ________ 6. morning ________
7. weather ________ 8. banned ________

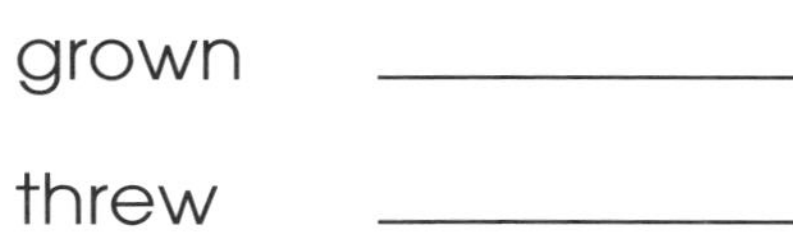

A. Mrs. Jenkins has 3 triangular flower beds. Help her find the perimeter and the angles of each flower bed. Then write "scalene", "isosceles", or "equilateral" to name the shape of each flower bed.

1.

A

5.8 m 5.8 m

B 3 m C

Flower Bed for Roses

Perimeter = 14.6 m

∠ A = 8.8 ∠ B = 3 ∠ C = 8.8.

Shape: a/an __________ triangle

2.

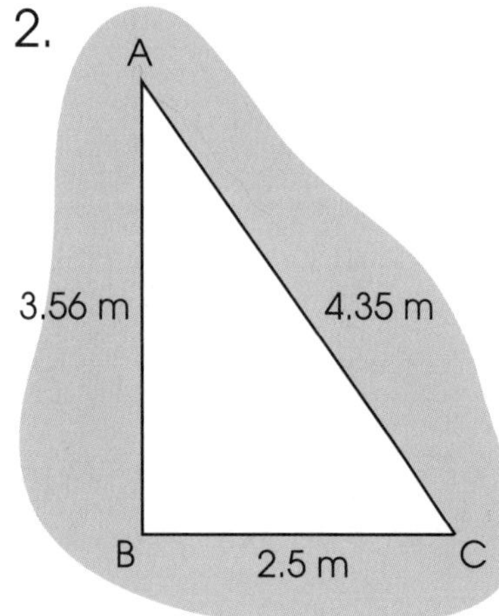

Flower Bed for Tulips

Perimeter = 9 m

∠ A = 7m ∠ B = 5m ∠ C = 6m

Shape: a/an __________ triangle

3.

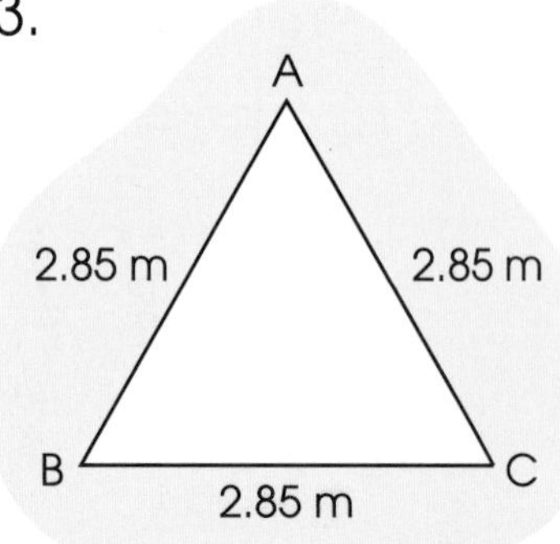

Flower Bed for Daisies

Perimeter = 6 m

∠ A = 4 ∠ B = 4 ∠ C = 4

Shape: a/an __________ triangle

Week 1

Mathematics

B. Mrs. Jenkins uses a number line to show how she plants the flowers. Write a decimal number to indicate how far each flower is from the post. Then answer the questions.

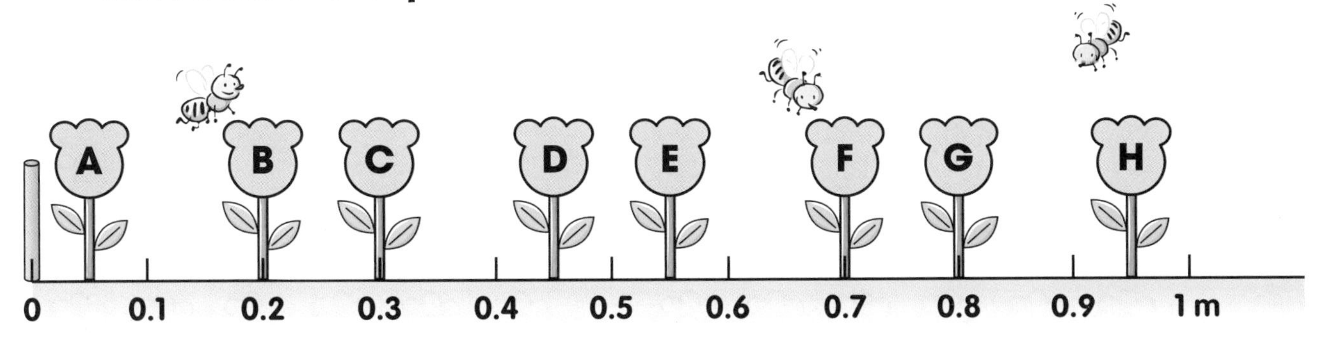

1. Post to Flower

   A: 0.1 m

   B: 0.2 m

   C: 0.3 m

   D: 0.4 m

   E: 0.5 m

   F: 0.6 m

   G: 0.7 m

   H: 0.8 m

2. Distance between A and B: 0.2

3. Distance between D and G: 0.4

4. Number of flowers within 0.5 m of the post: 4

5. The rule that Mrs. Jenkins follows to plant her flowers:

C. Write 2 equivalent fractions for the pink flowers in each set.

1.

12/16 = 24/32

2.

8/20   16/40

3.

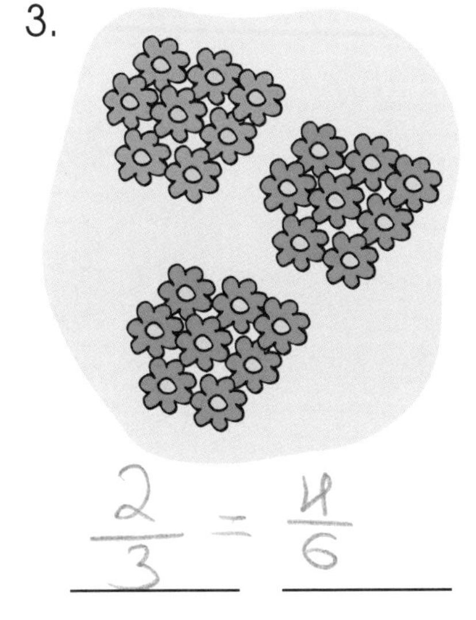

2/3 = 4/6

D. Colour the flowers. Then fill in the blanks with fractions to complete the sentences.

1.

$1\frac{1}{3}$ groups of the flowers are red, $\frac{1}{6}$ group is pink, and the rest are purple.

$\frac{1}{9}$ of a group of flowers is purple.

2.

- $\frac{3}{4}$ group is pink
- $1\frac{1}{2}$ groups are purple
- the rest are yellow

$\frac{2}{8}$ of a group of flowers is yellow.

3.

- 1.2 groups are yellow
- 0.3 group is red
- the rest are purple

0.5 of a group of flowers is purple.

Week 1

Mathematics

E. Help Mrs. Jenkins solve the problems.

1.

8 flowers have 96 petals.

2. Total weight: 1150 g

Each bag weighs 150 g.

3. Each row has 24 flowers. There are 432 flowers in 18 rows.

4. There are 1275 flowers in the garden. If 865 flowers are red, 410 flowers are not red.

5. There are 3 flower beds with a total of 1275 flowers in the garden. On average, there are 425 flowers in each flower bed.

6. If Mrs. Jenkins waters the flowers with 25.65 L of water every week, she will use 128.25 L of water in 5 weeks.

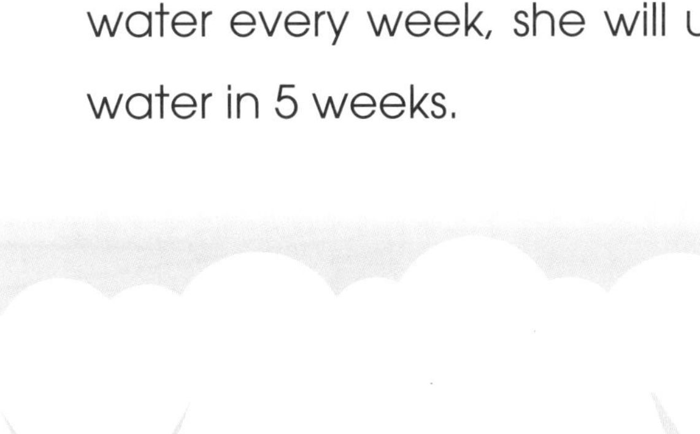

Week 1

Science

A. Name the energy sources and match them with the correct pictures.

water biomass nuclear oil
solar energy wind coal

Energy Source

- Oil ; (A)
  a fossil fuel extracted from the ground by mining
- Solar energy ; (G)
  comes from the sun's rays
- wind ; (F)
  comes from moving air
- water ; (E)
  comes from the natural flow of water
- Biomass ; (D)
  energy released by a nuclear reaction
- coal ; (C)
  formed under layers of mud that cover the remains of organic matter
- nuclear ; ( )
  plant material and animal waste that contain stored energy

B. Circle the correct words to complete the chart. Then identify whether each energy source is renewable or non-renewable.

1.

Two Kinds of Energy Sources

Renewable Energy Sources

generated by natural / human-made resources that will never / eventually run out

Non-renewable Energy Sources

can / cannot be replaced quickly and have a limited / unlimited supply

2.

coal solar energy wind biomass

a. 

Wind ;

Renewable energy source

b. 

Coal ;

non Renewable

c. 

Solar energy ;

Renewable

d. 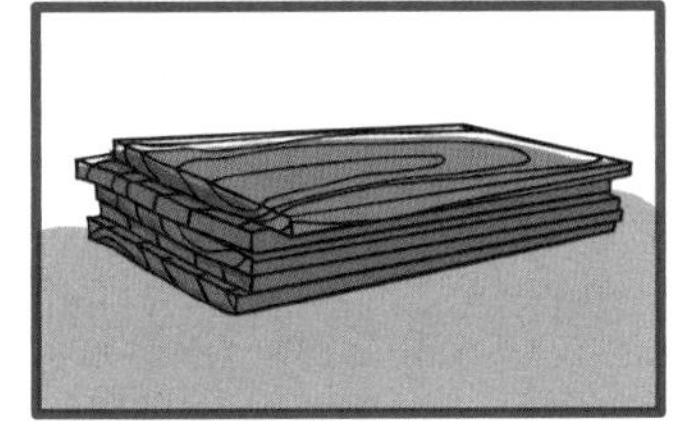

biomass ;

non-Renewable

A. Circle the correct symbols of Canada.

Symbols of Canada

1. This animal is a symbol of Canada's fur trade.

2. This is Canada's national sport.

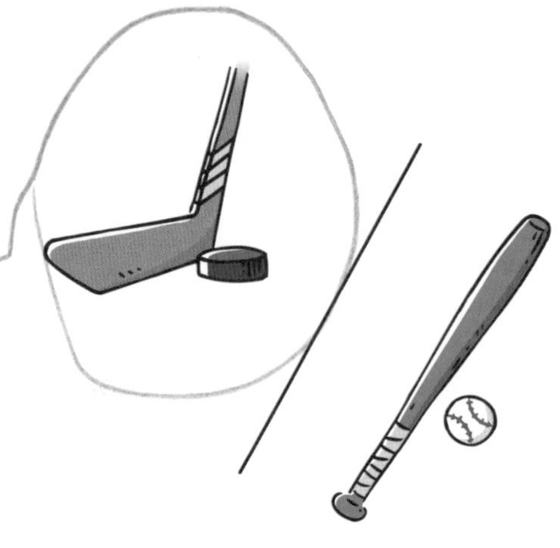

3. This animal symbolizes the traits that Canadians value: strength, courage, persistence, and intelligence.

4. This flies on all government buildings.

5. This is home to Canada's federal government.

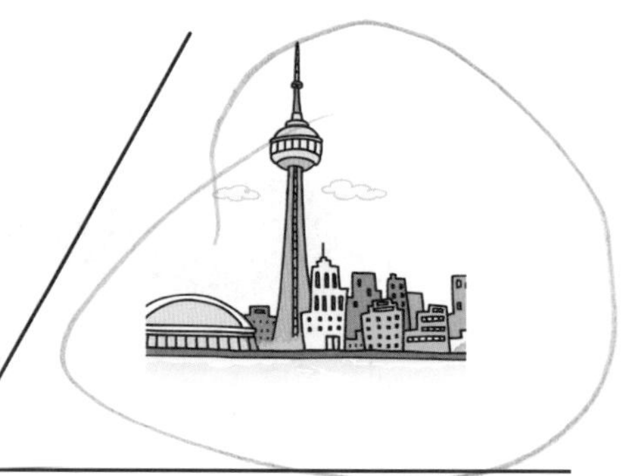

B. Colour the 🍁 if the sentences are true.

1. Red and white are the official colours of Canada.
2. The grain elevator represents the strong agricultural heritage of Nunavut.

3. Lacrosse is Canada's national summer sport.

4. Canada is a multicultural country that accepts people of all ethnic backgrounds and languages.

5. English is the only official language of Canada.

C. Draw another symbol of Canada and write what it represents.

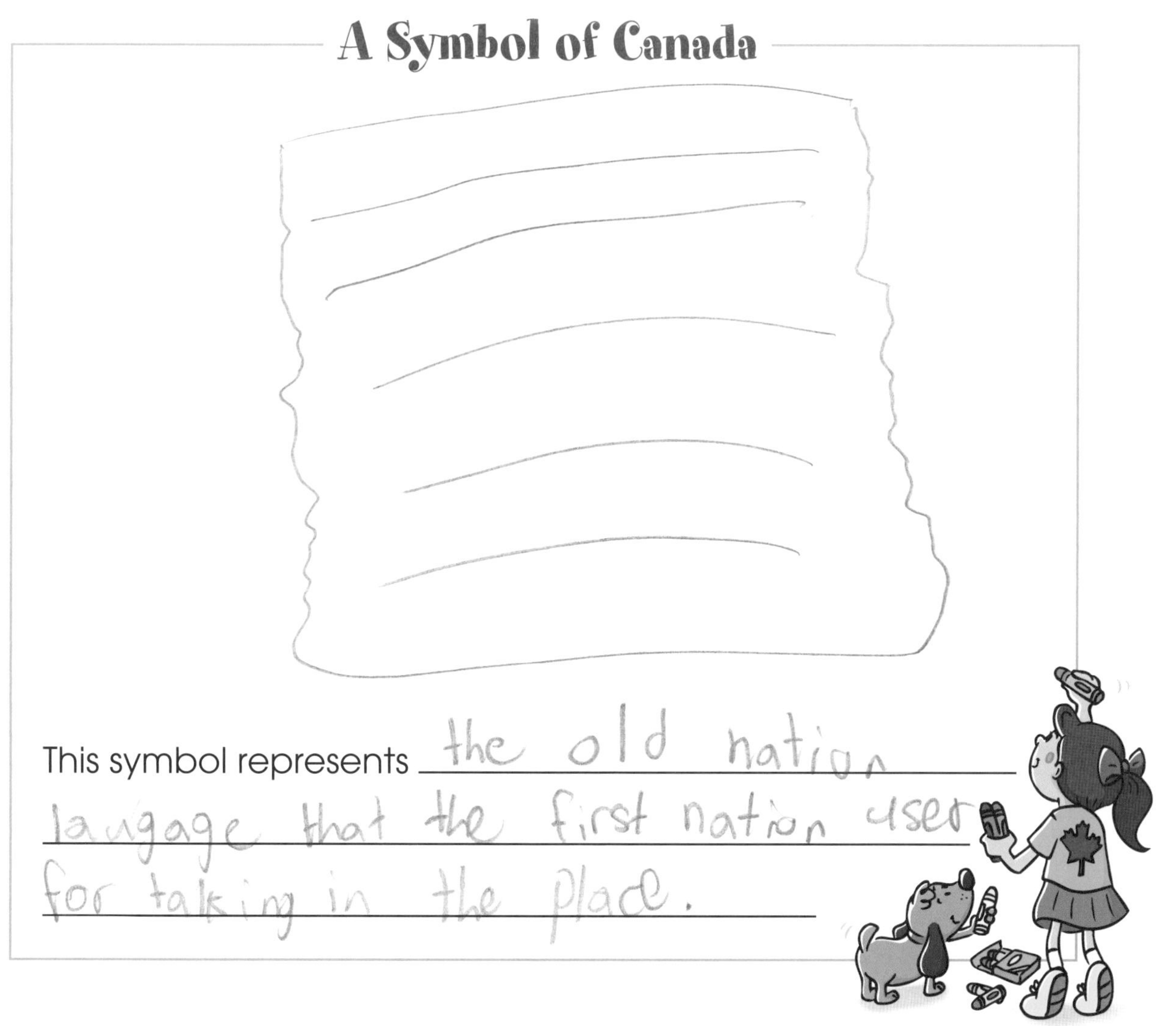

This symbol represents the old nation langage that the first nation user for taking in the place.

Week 2

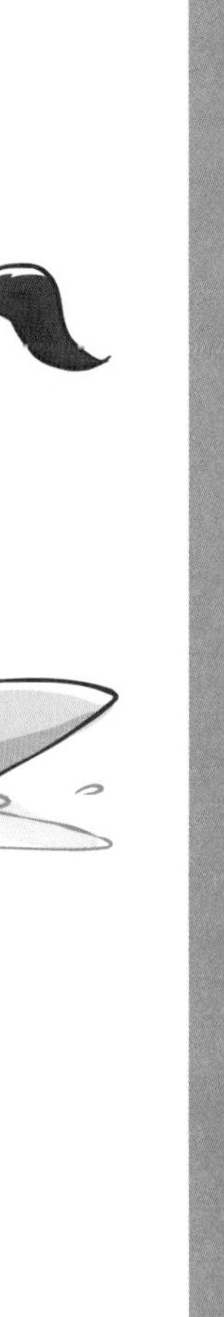

English

- read a passage and answer questions
- identify proper nouns and common nouns
- combine pairs of simple sentences to form complex sentences
- write a persuasive letter

Mathematics

- write amounts in decimals and in words
- count and draw money
- find probabilities
- group coins and solve problems

Science

- identify internal and external forces and their different types
- review how different structures can withstand natural forces

Social Studies

- learn about Canada's early settlers and immigrants

* The Canadian penny is no longer in circulation. It is used in the unit to show money amounts to the cent.

Week 2 A English

A. Read the passage.

Roller coasters have certainly **evolved** over time. The first roller coasters appeared in Russia in the 16th **century**. They were called "scream machines". These roller coasters were simply wooden sleds that slid down an icy five-storey hill in the winter.

In the 19th century, small wheels were attached to the bottoms of these sleds. However, no **emphasis** was placed on safety and as a result, many people were injured when the carts began to fly off the tracks. As the years passed, improvements were made on the track, locking wheels, and lift cables for the carts.

By the end of the 1800s, circular loop rides had emerged and amusement parks became popular. However, when the Great Depression struck in 1929, people lost their jobs and had no money for leisure activities. The amusement park industry was in dire straits.

In 1955, Walt Disney brought a remarkable change to the business when he opened Disneyland in California. Before long, theme parks were opening again and a variety of roller coaster designs were created.

Today, the latest roller coasters can reach incredible speeds of approximately 190 kilometres per hour. They can also have drops of roughly 120 metres, tracks as long as 850 metres, and angles of **ascent** and descent up to 90 degrees!

Regardless of the type of roller coaster, it is obvious from the sounds and the faces of the riders that every individual experiences a different sensation. Some look as though they have just seen a ghost, others look like their stomach has been invaded by aliens, and some are laughing uncontrollably, like they have had the time of their lives. Which is it for you?

B. Find the effect of each event in the passage.

Event	Effect
In the 16th century, Russians slid down an icy hill on wooden sleds.	
No emphasis was placed on the safety of the "scream machines".	
Circular loop rides emerged in the 1800s.	
During the Great Depression, many people lost their jobs.	
Walt Disney opened Disneyland in 1955.	

C. Match the definitions with the words in bold from the passage.

1. **evolved**

2. **century**

3. **emphasis**

4. **ascent**

upward motion
developed
one hundred years
importance

D. Circle the proper nouns and underline the common nouns in the sentences.

A proper noun refers to a specific person, place, or thing.

Katie has a dog. ← **A common noun** refers to any person, place, or thing.

1. The cost of building just one roller coaster is well into millions of dollars.

2. Cedar Point and Six Flags Magic Mountain are among the leading roller coaster amusement parks in the world.

3. Standing over 30 storeys high, "The Supreme Scream" is one of the world's tallest free fall rides.

4. One of the scientific principles behind how roller coasters move is based on gravity, which was discovered by Sir Isaac Newton.

E. Combine each pair of simple sentences to form a complex sentence.

1. Many people enjoy riding on roller coasters. They derive a lot of excitement from the rides.

____

____

2. The Great Depression struck in 1929. The amusement park industry had to close down.

____

____

F. Check the correct answers.

1. The first roller coasters were:

   (A) sleds with wheels

   (B) sleds on tracks

   (C) sleds

2. *The amusement park business went downhill because of:*

   (A) World War I

   (B) the Great Depression

   (C) lack of lumber

3. Walt Disney is credited for:

   (A) sleds

   (B) reviving theme parks

   (C) sleds with wheels

4. The first roller coaster appeared in:

   (A) Asia (B) Russia

   (C) Canada

G. Write a letter to your parents to persuade them to let you go on the fastest, highest, and scariest roller coaster in the world.

Highest!

Fastest!

Scariest!

A. See how much Jimmy saved last week. Help him write the amount he saved each day in decimals and words. Then answer the questions.

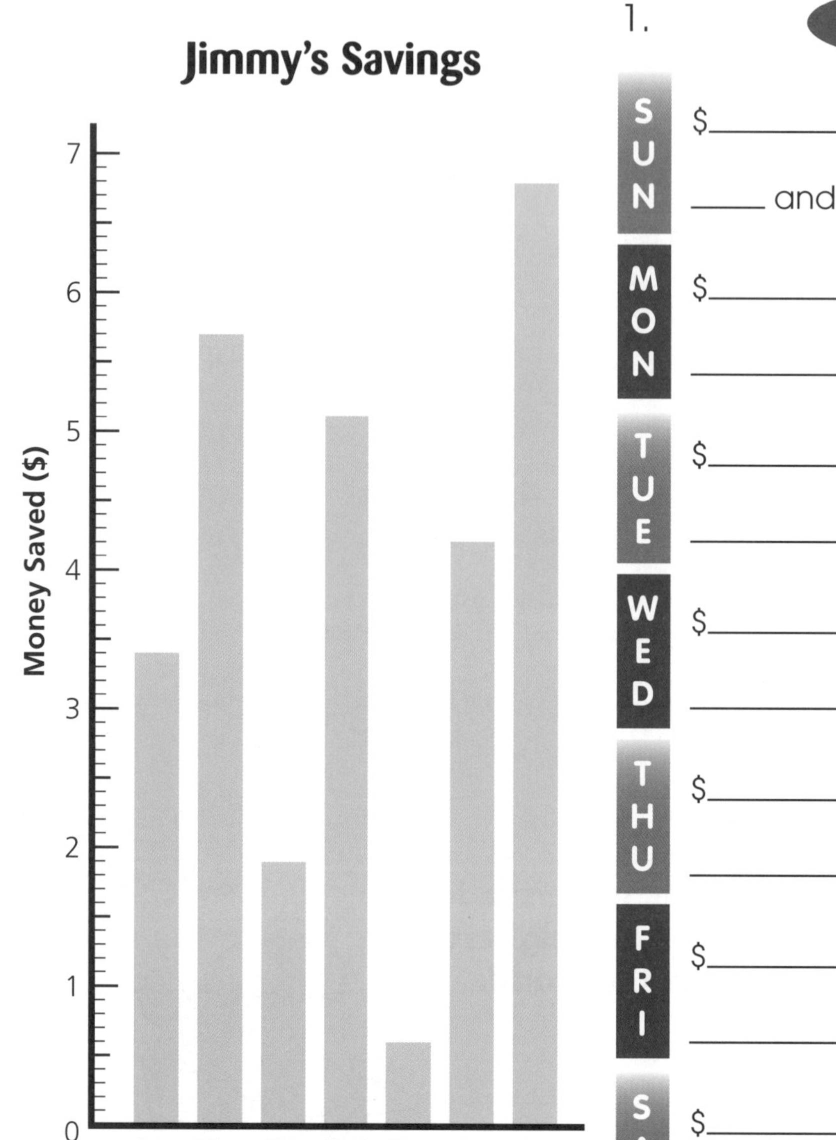

1. *Record*

SUN $________ ;
____ and ____ hundredths dollars

MON $________ ;
______________________ dollars

TUE $________ ;
______________________ dollars

WED $________ ;
______________________ dollars

THU $________ ;
______________________ dollars

FRI $________ ;
______________________ dollars

SAT $________ ;
______________________ dollars

2. How much did Jimmy save

   a. on the weekend? ______

   b. from Monday to Friday? ______

   c. last week? ______

3. If Jimmy trades all his money for $5 bills, how many $5 bills will he get?

Week 2

Mathematics

B. Write the costs or draw the fewest bills and coins needed to pay for the items. Then fill in the blanks.

1.

2.

3.

4.

5. Name the two items that cost more than $200.

necklece, camera
____

____

6. The price difference between the most and the least expensive items is:

____

7.

88.8
____

C. **A store is having a sale. Jimmy picks a card to see how much he can save. Help Jimmy solve the problems.**

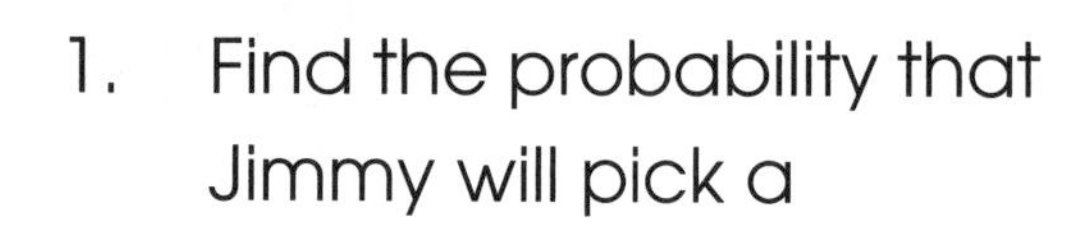

1. Find the probability that Jimmy will pick a

   a. $5 off : likley

   b. $10 off : Probbbly

   c. $40 off : un likly

   d. card that will save him $10 or more: prolabe

2. *I bought this toy car.* $89.66

   a. If Tom picks a $5 off, how much does he need to pay?

   84.66

   b. If Tom pays $49.66, which card did he pick?

Week 2 Mathematics

D. The children pay for their items with the bags of coins. Help them draw the number of bags needed to pay for each item. Then write the matching number sentence and solve the problems.

1.

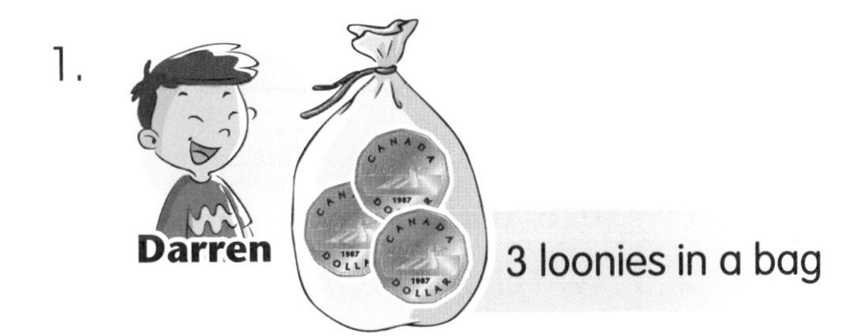

a.

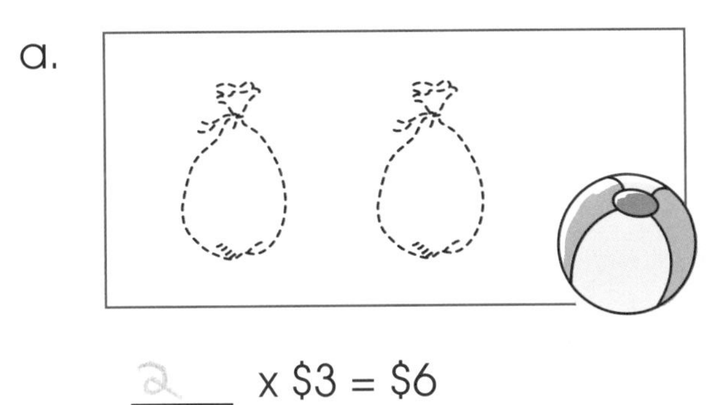

2 x $3 = $6

b.

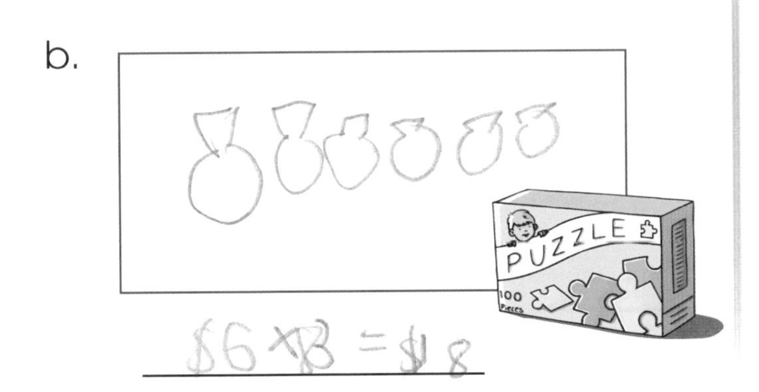

$6 x 3 = $18

2.

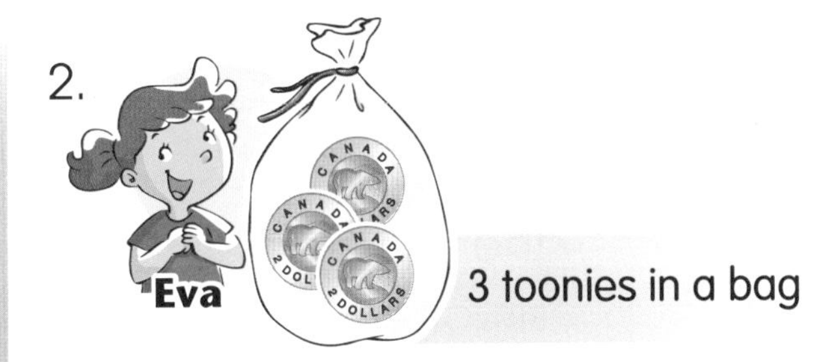

a.

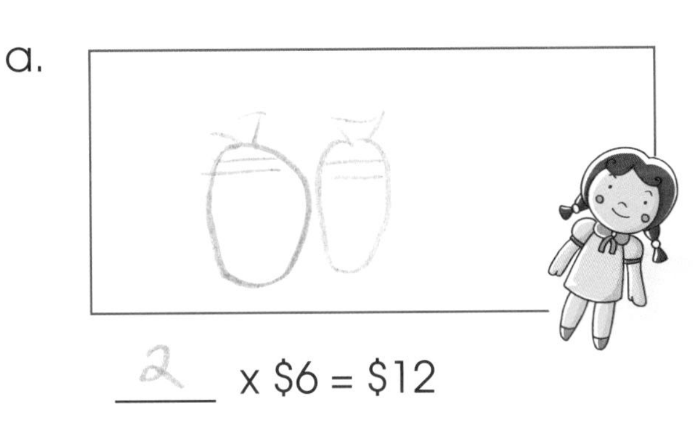

2 x $6 = $12

b.

$4 x $6 = $24

3.

No. of Bags Needed / Purchase	ball, car	teddy bear, doll	puzzle, ball
Darren	___	___	___
Eva	___	___	___

A. Write whether the forces are "internal" or "external" and fill in the blanks with the given words. Then identify the types of internal and external forces in the pictures.

live load dead load compression tension

Force

1. ______________ force

the force that acts on a structure from the outside

Types : ______________

____

furniture
______________ load

brick
______________ load

door
______________ load

2. ______________ force

the force that acts from within the structure

Types : ______________

____

B. Fill in the blanks to show what techniques are used to build safer structures.

Earthquake	*Flood*	*High Wind*
crisscrossing	drainage	shutters
flexible	higher	roof
steel	masts	inward

1.

- Use a. flexible materials so that they bend rather than break under impact.
- Construct buildings with b. crisscrossing frames.
- Reinforce walls with c. steel bars.

2.

- Install a foundation a. drainage system.
- Buildings can be built on b. higher ground or on steel c. masts so that they are lifted off the ground.

3.

- Install a. shutters on the windows.
- Have doors open b. inwards rather than outward.
- Tie the c. roof to the walls to prevent it from getting blown off.

A. Identify Canada's early settlers and immigrants.

Canada's Early Settlers and Immigrants

countries   Black Loyalists   French   Irish

1.

British and French explorers sailed to what would become Canada to explore new land.

2.

black loyalist came to Canada to escape the American Revolution and slavery.

3.

Irish immigrants came to Canada to escape famine and poverty in Ireland.

4.

Encouraged by the Canadian Multiculturalism Act, people from different countries around the world came to seek freedom and equality in every aspect of life.

Week 2 Social Studies

B. Circle the correct words to learn more about other groups of early immigrants to Canada.

1. Between 1868 and 1964, a large number of **poor / rich** and orphaned British children were sent to Canada. Some of them were **hired / adopted** by kind families, while others were exploited and had to work on farms for long hours.

2. Chinese immigrants came to Canada as early as the late **1850s / 2010s** . They came to dig for **gold / coal** in the Fraser Canyon Gold Rush in British Columbia. In 1881, there was another influx of Chinese workers who came to seek **investment / job** opportunities with the Canadian Pacific Railway, which was being built to connect the east and west coasts of Canada.

3. Early Japanese immigrants came to Canada in the late 19th century and settled in British Columbia. Many of them were farmers and **teachers / fishermen** . After Japan attacked Pearl Harbour, Hawaii in 1941, the Japanese Canadians were seen as a threat and were sent to internment **camps / schools** . In 1988, the **federal / municipal** government officially apologized for the mistreatment of the Japanese Canadians.

English

- read a story and separate the paragraphs
- decide whether the statements are facts or opinions
- identify synonyms from the passage and find them in a word search
- decide whether sentences are in the active or passive voice

Mathematics

- find the total cost of each group of items
- find the prices of different meal combos
- use a spinner to discuss probability
- complete a bar graph

Science

- identify the mechanical advantage of simple machines
- review the three classes of levers

Social Studies

- identify different communities in Canada
- learn about Canada's ethnic neighbourhoods

* The Canadian penny is no longer in circulation. It is used in the unit to show money amounts to the cent.

A. Nicole forgot to use paragraphs in her letter. Read the letter and put the paragraph symbol "¶" before each sentence where a new paragraph is needed. (Hint: There are 6 paragraphs.)

Back to Nature

Dear Mom and Dad,

Adriana and I are having a fantastic time at Uncle Ross and Aunt Joyce's. It is like paradise here, with a view overlooking the water called "Satellite Channel" (not the television kind, Dad). I'm learning to really appreciate wildlife and the outdoors. Yesterday, while on the charter plane from Vancouver to Victoria, we were amazed to spot a pod of approximately 20 orcas, with their dorsal fins piercing through the water each time they surfaced. It was an incredible sight! Did you know that pods of the resident killer whales are made up of the mother's immediate and extended family members? They may stay together as a family even after they're fully grown and can live anywhere from 50 to 80 years. Today, we saw a number of sea lions and otters frolicking in the water. It was quite peculiar to see one otter lying on its back; it had a stone on its belly and a scallop in its paw. We discovered afterwards that otters float on their backs while they crack open the seashell of their prey with a rock. You won't believe this - there's a pair of bald eagles nesting in Aunt Joyce and Uncle Ross's very own backyard. It's astounding to see the eagles swooping in at speeds of up to 160 kilometres per hour. They can spot fish from about 1.5 kilometres away! The term "eagle eyes" is no joke. Aunt Joyce doesn't mind the eagles hanging out in their fir trees, but she does get frustrated with the deer and rabbits that come on their grounds often. These sneaky vegetarians arrive after dusk, having already eaten their main meal in nearby fields, only to enjoy Aunt Joyce's roses and lilies for dessert. I guess they feel comfortable trespassing on the property, since there is no dog to frighten them off. Tomorrow, Uncle Ross is taking us on an excursion to Johnstone Strait, where he is confident that we will see a pod or two of orcas. Apparently in July and August, the number of whales in this area peaks due to the salmon passing through (one of their favourite foods). They naturally make this one of their main foraging territories. I'll give you more details when I get home.

Love,
Nicole

B. Indicate whether each of the following is a fact (F) or an opinion (O).

1. One way to travel from Vancouver to Victoria is by charter plane. F
2. Uncle Ross and Aunt Joyce's house is like a holiday resort. F
3. Otters use rocks to crack open the hard shells of prey. F
4. Bald eagles can see from a distance of 1.5 kilometres. F
5. Many orcas come to Johnstone Straight during the salmon season. O
6. You need to go to Victoria, B.C. if you want to truly experience animals in their natural habitats. O

C. Read the quotes from Nicole's letter and answer the questions.

1\.

"It was an incredible sight!"

What did Nicole see?

____

____

2\.

"The term 'eagle eyes' is no joke."

Why did Nicole make this remark?

____

____

3\.

"These sneaky vegetarians..."

What were they?

____

____

D. Read the clues and match them with synonyms from the passage. Then find these synonyms in the word search.

Synonym

1. amazing

   ____

2. unusual/strange

   ____

3. unbelievable

   ____

4. searching

   ____

5. diving

   ____

6. back

   ____

7. playing

   ____

8. secretive

   ____

a	t	o						y	b
a	e	r	o	a	t	n	o	w	e
s	q	o	b	d	o	r	s	a	l
e	h	i	k	c	t	n	n	s	m
l	k	n	t	i	s	i	e	t	f
m	i	n	o	k	w	e	a	o	r
a	n	e	r	f	o	h	k	u	o
e	c	g	e	r	o	n	y	n	t
m	r	o	i	o	p	v	i	d	y
p	e	c	u	l	i	a	r	i	a
e	d	f	t	i	n	s	d	n	r
t	i	o	r	c	g	e	v	g	p
e	b	r	e	k	v	b	t	e	u
n	l	a	b	i	i	a	p	b	y
b	e	g	i	n	c	t	e	r	p
g	a	i	p	g					
i	a	n	t	a					
v	n	g	t	y					

E. Write "A" for sentences in the active voice and "P" for sentences in the passive voice.

Active Voice

The spider scared the boy.
The subject is performing an action.

Passive Voice

The boy was scared by the spider.
The subject is being acted upon.

1. I was caught by surprise! P
2. The deer ate grass in the nearby fields. A
3. The scallop was eaten by the otter. P
4. The deer was scared away by the dog. A
5. The otter cracked open the shell of a scallop with a rock. A
6. We went from Vancouver to Victoria by charter plane. P

F. Rewrite the sentences by changing them from the active voice to the passive voice and vice versa.

Active
Voice
Passive

(A) The bald eagle spotted a big fish.

(B) Uncle Ross took us to the shore in his van.

(C) A hearty meal was prepared for us by Aunt Joyce.

(A) a big fish spotted the bald eagle

(B) ______

(C) ______

Week 3

Mathematics

A. Sabrina is going grocery shopping with her mother. Help her find the total cost of each group of items and the total amount of juice.

1. Cost of 5 jars of peanut butter:

____

2. Cost of 4 cartons of milk:

____

3. Cost of 7 packs of batteries:

____

4. *Cost of 3 tins of coffee:*

____

5. ***Total Cost of Juice***

____

Total Amount of Juice

____

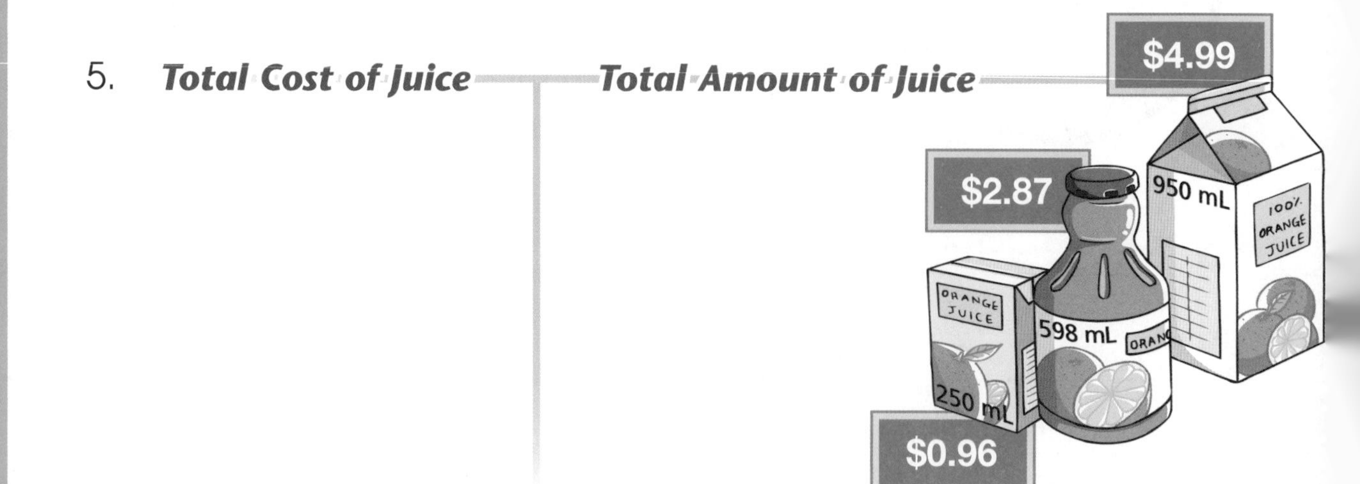

B. Look at the price list. Find the price of each combo.

C. **Look at the spinners. Measure the angles to complete the charts. Then find the possible outcomes of the spinners and answer the questions.**

1.

Spinner A

Sector	Angle
top	
yo-yo	
doll	
car	

Spinner B

Sector	Angle
top	
car	
doll	

Possible outcomes:

____

Possible outcomes:

____

2. Find the probability that

a. Spinner A will land on  :

____

b. Spinner B will land on  :

____

3.

____

D. Complete the bar graph to show the outcomes of Spinner B after 100 spins. Then answer the questions.

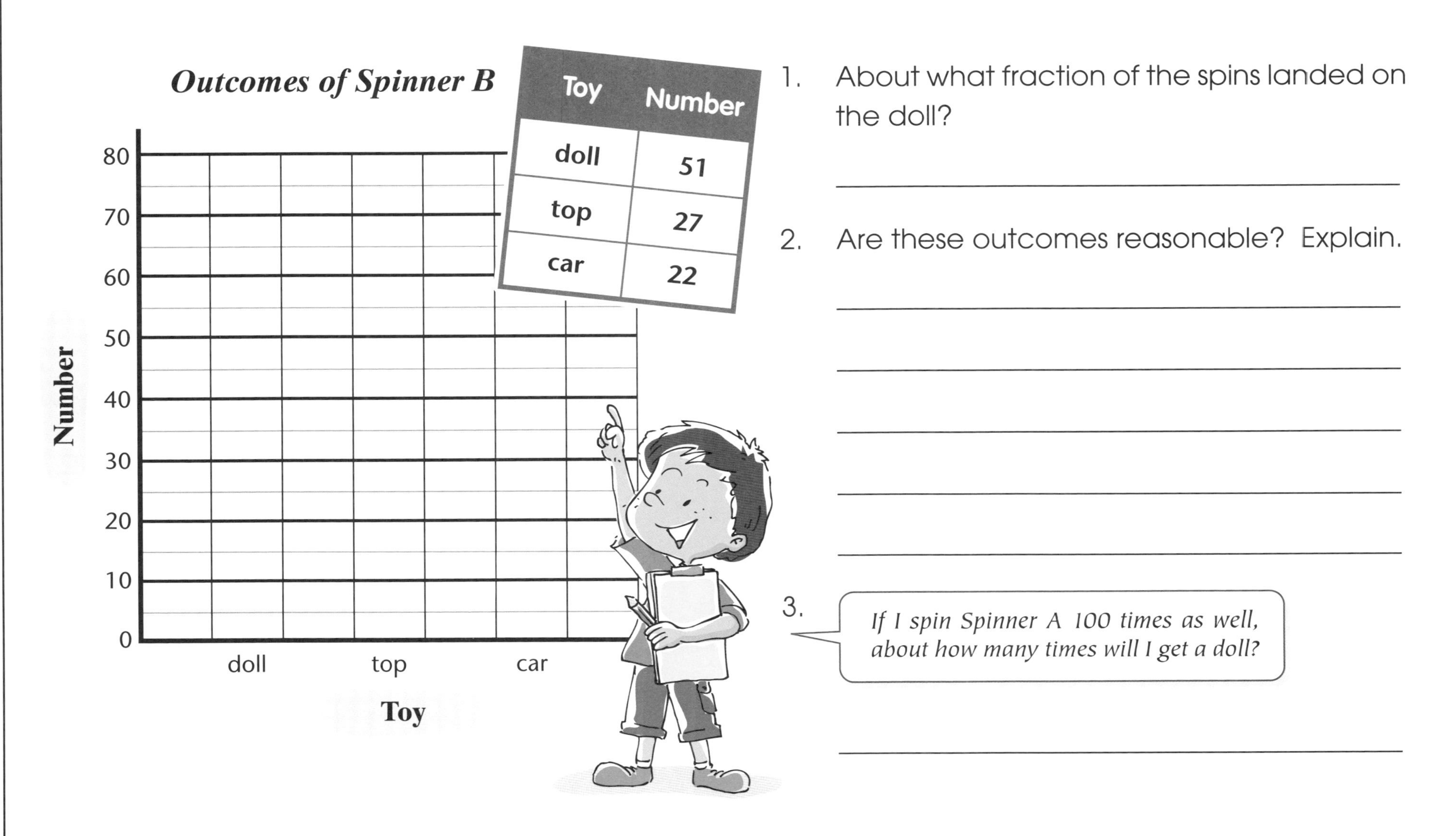

Toy	Number
doll	51
top	27
car	22

1. About what fraction of the spins landed on the doll?

____

2. Are these outcomes reasonable? Explain.

____

3. *If I spin Spinner A 100 times as well, about how many times will I get a doll?*

____

A. **Circle the correct words to describe the mechanical advantage of these machines. Then write "G" for the picture that has greater mechanical advantage and "L" for the one with less.**

Mechanical Advantage

Lever: A lever that has its fulcrum closer to the load has greater / less mechanical advantage.

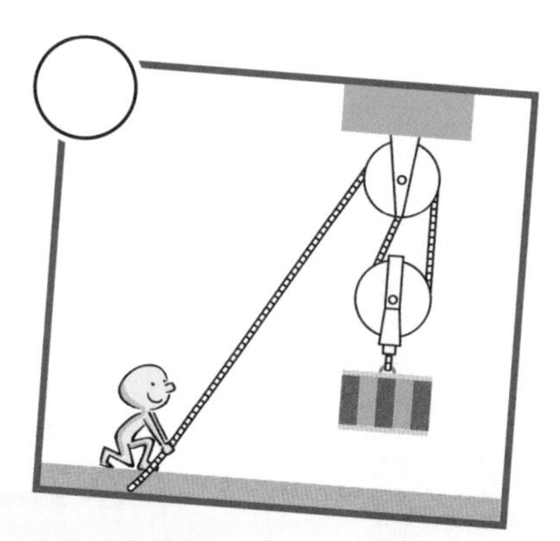

Pulley: A pulley system that consists of more pulleys has greater / less mechanical advantage.

Inclined Plane: A longer inclined plane has greater / less mechanical advantage.

B. Fill in the blanks to complete the descriptions of the three classes of levers. Check the examples that belong to each class. Then identify the lever shown in the picture and label the parts.

Three Classes of Levers

First-class Lever:

The ____________ is between the load and the effort.

e.g. (A) scissors (B) nutcracker
(C) tweezers (D) see-saw

Second-class Lever:

The ____________ is between the fulcrum and the effort.

e.g. (A) broom (B) nail clipper
(C) nutcracker (D) bottle-opener

Third-class Lever:

The ____________ is between the load and the fulcrum.

e.g. (A) broom (B) wheelbarrow
(C) scissors (D) fishing rod

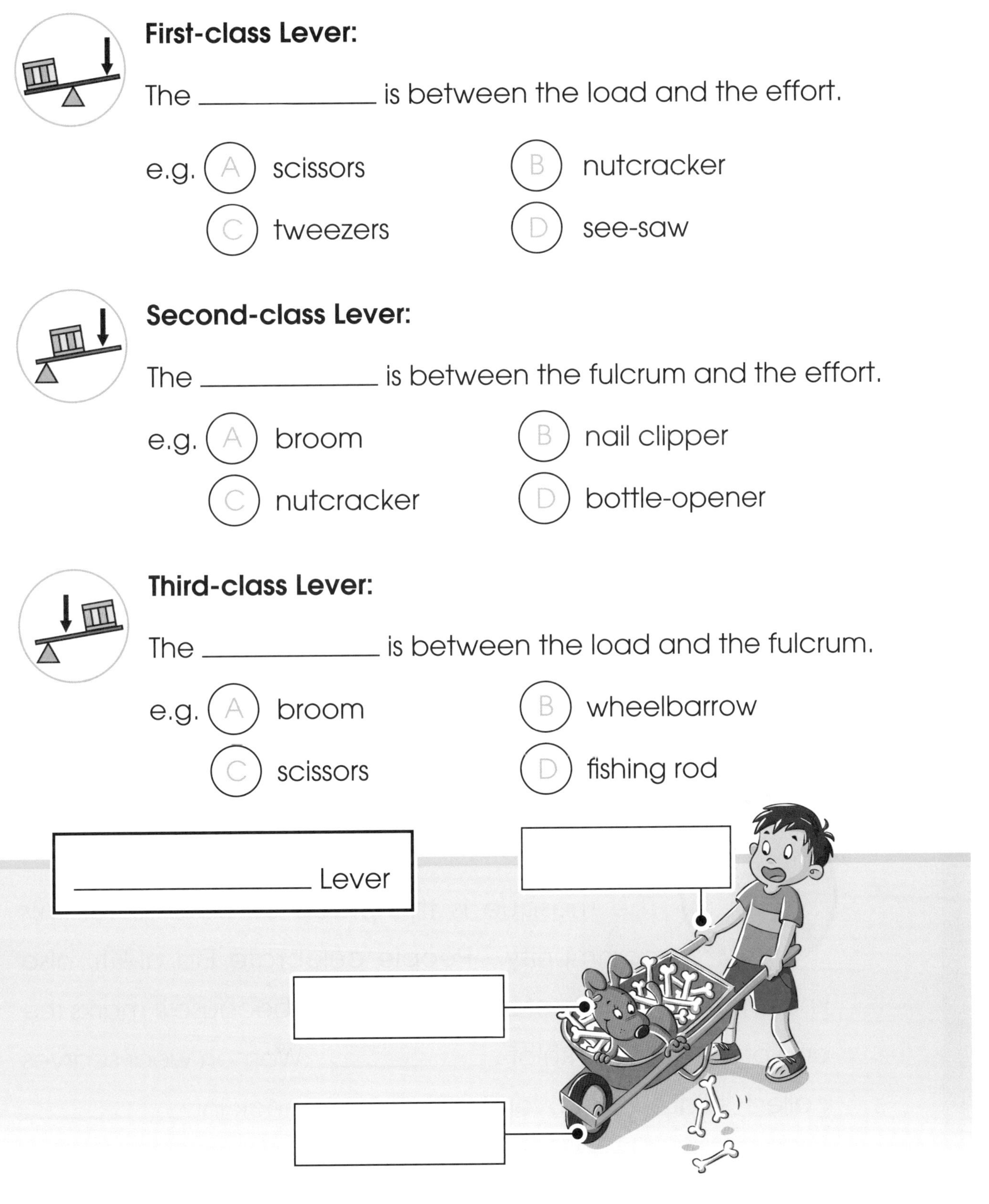

Week 3

Social Studies

A. Identify the communities in Canada and fill in the blanks to complete the descriptions.

Mennonite	plain	public
Muslim	worship	fasting
Jewish	horses	pray

Different communities, with their unique cultures and beliefs, help shape Canada's multicultural identity.

1. **J**__________ Community

The synagogue is the place of __________ for this community. To show their respect and reverence, men and boys wear small skullcaps called "kippahs" when they __________ or enter a synagogue. Passover is a very important festival celebrated by this community.

2. **Me**__________ Community

People of this community wear simple and __________ clothing. They live traditional farm lives and do not use modern technology or electricity. They travel around using __________ and buggies.

3. **Mu**__________ Community

The mosque is the place of worship for this community. People celebrate Eid al-Fitr, also known as the Festival of Breaking the Fast because it marks the end of the holy month of __________ . Women wear scarves called "hijabs" to cover the head and neck in __________ places.

B. Match the ethnic neighbourhoods with the descriptions. Write the letters in the circles.

Canada's multiculturalism is also reflected in the many ethnic neighbourhoods across the country. Let's take a look at some examples in Toronto.

- **A** Little India
- **B** Little Italy
- **C** Chinatown
- **D** Greektown

- red is a prevalent colour as it symbolizes good luck
- restaurants serving traditional dim sum and other authentic dishes
- the Dragon Dance Parade held during Chinese New Year

- specialty shops selling brightly-coloured saris, jewellery, and spices
- restaurants serving authentic Indian, Pakistani, Sri Lankan, and Bangladeshi cuisines
- the Festival of South Asia held every summer

- blue and white flags and signs along the street
- restaurants serving authentic souvlaki
- shops selling a variety of cheese and olives
- the Taste of the Danforth festival held every summer

- street signs and flags in green, white, and red
- cafés and family-style restaurants serving pizza, pasta, and gelato
- annual Taste of Little Italy festival held in summer

Arts & Crafts

- make a mummy

Comics

- The King's Secret

Fun Places to Go in Summer

- Dinosaur Provincial Park

MUMMY

Week
4

Arts & Crafts

Materials:

- water
- paint
- white glue
- long balloon
- wallpaper paste
- aluminum foil
- bucket or bowl
- newspaper torn in strips

Directions:

1. Mix paste and water until mixture has consistency of sour cream.
2. Blow up balloon and tie. Then wrap aluminum foil around balloon.
3. Dip strips of newspaper into wallpaper paste.
4. Wrap strips around "mummy" until it looks like the shape of a mummy. Let it dry.
5. Seal case with coat of white glue. Let it dry.
6. Paint mummy case and draw traditional mask.

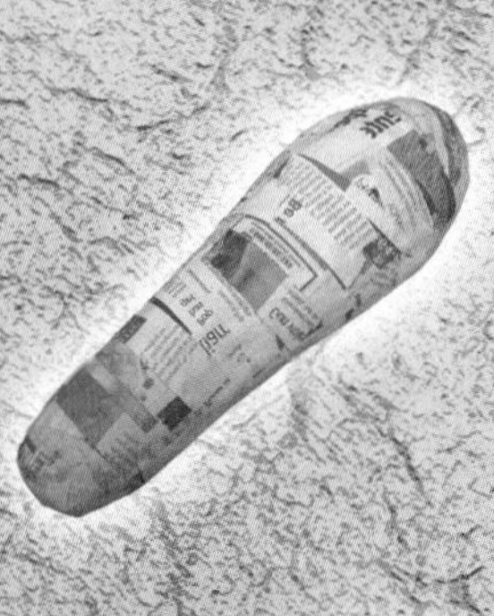

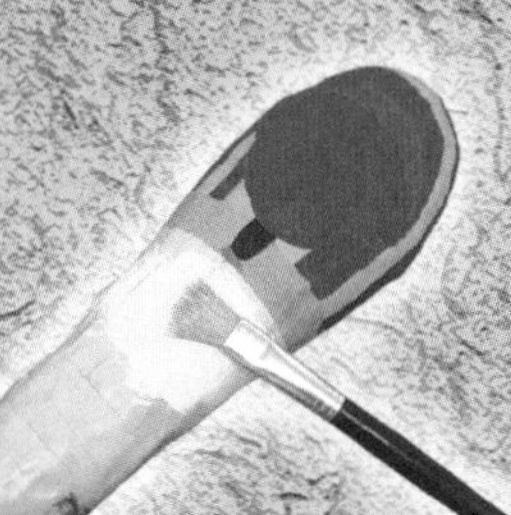

COMICS
The King's Secret
Long ago, there was a king whose wife gave birth to a baby boy.
Oh...let me hold my baby boy.

The king was pleased. But when he saw his son, he was shocked.
His...his...ears...
His son had the ears of an ox.

The barber promised to keep it a secret, but from then on, his tummy kept growing.

One day, the barber met a drummer. He was shocked to see the barber's big tummy.

The barber decided to tell the drummer the king's secret, even though he had promised to keep it.

Instantly, the barber's tummy shrunk to its normal size.

The king found out that his secret was out. He was very angry.

The barber apologized. Then he told the king that he should not be ashamed of his own son.

The king looked at his beautiful young boy.

He realized that a child is always a blessing, no matter how he looks.

DINOSAUR Provincial Park

Located in Calgary, Alberta, Dinosaur Provincial Park is a UNESCO World Heritage Site. The Park is situated in the valley of the Red Deer River, where 40 dinosaur species have been discovered and more than 500 specimens excavated.

Seventy-five million years ago, the landscape there was very different from what it is today, with lush forests covering a coastal plain. The low swampy land was a favourable habitat for a variety of animals, including dinosaurs. The conditions were also perfect for the preservation of their bones as fossils.

You can take part in many fun-filled events in the Park. The Fossil Safari, for example, provides a hands-on opportunity to discover the Park's rich fossil resources: you can learn the secrets of fossil-finding, as well as the techniques for identifying the remains of dinosaurs. Although you are allowed to discover fossils yourself, all materials must be left in the Park and cannot be taken away.

Week 5

English

- read a passage, fill in information, and answer questions
- form words by adding prefixes and suffixes to root words
- identify compound and complex sentences
- combine sentences to form complex sentences

Mathematics

- find the areas of irregular shapes
- find the volume of solids
- write equivalent fractions
- measure and draw angles

Science

- identify organs of the human body

Social Studies

- learn about children's rights

A. Read the passage.

Mission Possible!

Imagine yourself being 320 000 kilometres from home, floating in outer space, with only one chance to make it home. This may sound inconceivable, but it did happen on April 11, 1970 during the mission of Apollo 13.

The Apollo 13 mission to the moon was progressing uneventfully until an oxygen tank exploded. James Lovell, the mission's commander, transmitted the now famous line to Mission Control in Houston, Texas: "Houston, we have a problem..." Their primary spacecraft, Odyssey, was losing oxygen, power, and its ability to navigate. The trip to the moon's surface was cancelled and all efforts were directed to bringing the astronauts home safely. People all over the world were concerned and began to follow the story.

Eventually, the Odyssey was abandoned and all three astronauts – Lovell, Haise, and Swigert – moved into the Lunar Module (called Aquarius), which was built to land on the moon. The Lunar Module, however, was only built for two people and had enough supplies for two days, but the astronauts were going to have to stay there for four days! Food, electricity, and oxygen needed to be conserved if they were going to make it home alive. The astronauts were crammed, the temperature dropped to 5°C, and moisture was condensing. Since the electrical systems were shut down, the astronauts could not use the navigation system; they had to navigate using the stars. One mistake could send them hurdling out into space, never to return. With their accurate star readings and precise rocket burns, however, the astronauts managed to point Aquarius in the right direction: toward Earth.

The mission ended on April 17, 1970 with the safe splashdown of the capsule and crew into the Pacific Ocean.

B. Fill in the information. Then answer the questions.

The Apollo 13 Mission

Mission Objective: 1. The Apollo 13 misson to the moon was progressing uneverticken the oxegan tank exploaded

- 2. james lovell (commander)
- 3. Haise
- 4. Swigert

Launched on:

5. April 11 1970

Returned on:

6. April 17 1970

Primary spacecraft:

7. all three will survive.

Lunar Module:

8. fited 2 people for 2 day

9. Why was the Apollo 13 mission aborted?

it was aborted because one oxegen tank exploded

10. Why did the astronauts move into the Lunar Module?

the Odessy was losing its oxegen power, and its ability to navicate. thats why they moved to the lunar module.

11. What problems did the astronauts face when moving into the Lunar Module?

there needed only 2 people and the lunor module could only last for 2 days but they needed four days

12. How did they navigate when the electrical systems were shut down?

they navigited with the stars one promblem if folwing the wrong star they would be lost in Space forever, however they managed to point at the aquaris in the right direction toward earth

C. Find the words from the passage with the following definitions.

1. preserved ____________
2. unthinkable ____________
3. to direct on course ____________
4. exact ____________
5. passed on a message ____________

D. Build two words from each root word by adding a prefix, a suffix, or both.

Prefix	Root Word	Suffix
re pre	appear	ful er
dis un	conceive	ness less
co mis	event	ish able
in con	hope	ly est
over	happy	ance

appear

____

____

conceive

____

____

event

____

____

hope

____

____

happy

____

____

E. Determine whether the sentences are compound sentences or complex sentences. Write the letters under the correct headings.

A Three days before Apollo 13 was launched, Thomas K. Mattingly, command module pilot, was removed from the mission.

B Jack Swigert was Mattingly's backup and had only a few days of preparation before the launch.

Compound Sentence
Complex Sentence

C Mattingly was not on the Apollo 13 spacecraft, but he was on the ground in a simulator, making every effort to figure out how the crew could safely re-enter the Earth's atmosphere.

D After the capsule had splashed down safely in the Pacific Ocean, the crew was escorted to the meeting site in Hawaii.

F. Combine each pair of sentences to form a complex sentence.

A The astronauts had to rely on the stars for navigation. The navigation system on their spacecraft did not function properly.

B The Apollo 13 mission was progressing smoothly. Then one of the oxygen tanks exploded.

C People all over the world learned about the aborted mission. They became gravely concerned about the safety of the crew.

Complex Sentences

A ______________________________

____

B ______________________________

____

C ______________________________

____

A. Help Amy and Eli find the area of each letter in their name. Then answer the questions.

1.

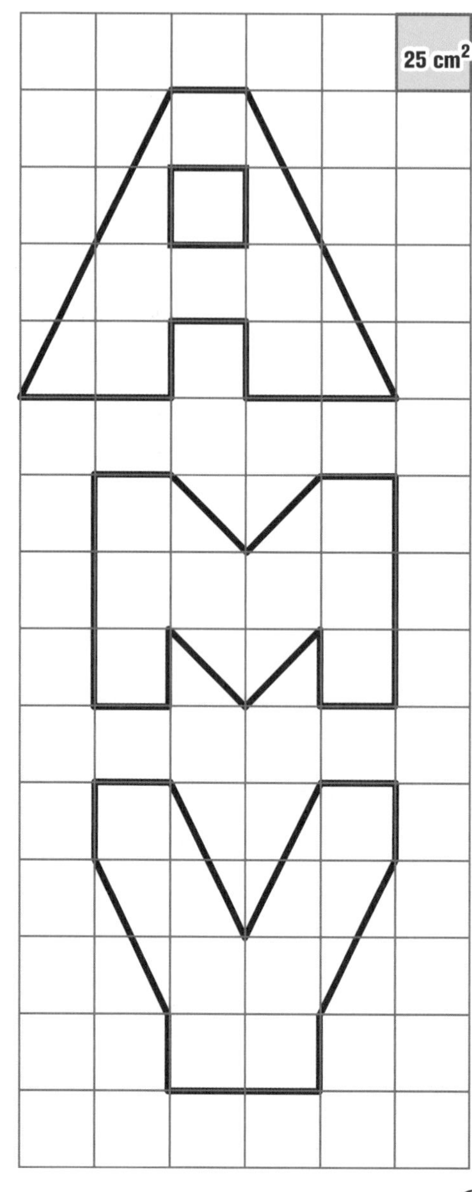

Area

A = ______ cm^2

M = ______ cm^2

Y = ______ cm^2

2.

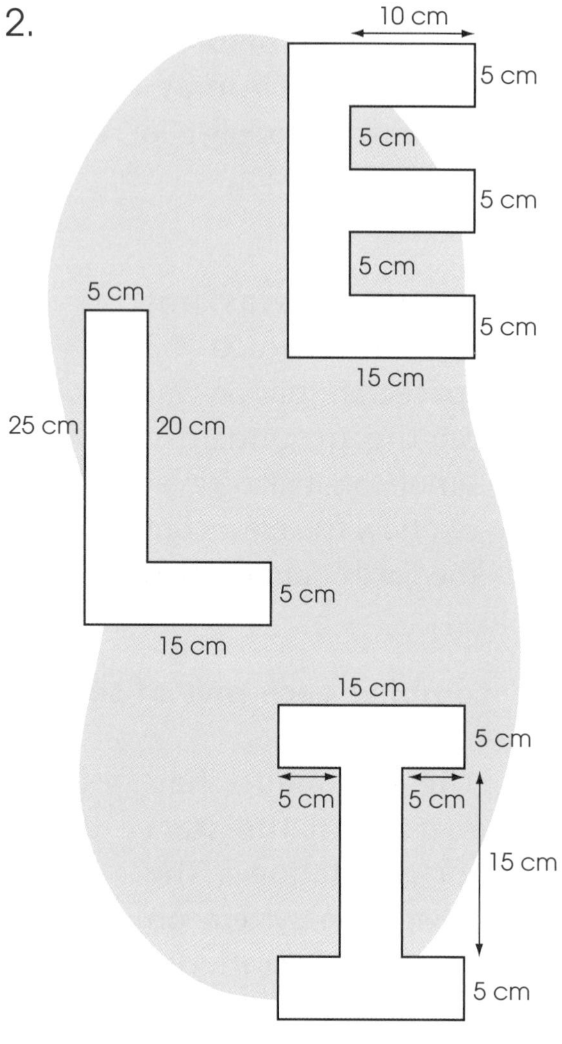

Area

E = ______ cm^2

L = ______ cm^2

I = ______ cm^2

A roll of lace is 1 m long and I need 88.5 cm for each letter. I need ______ rolls of lace.

If I put a string around the border of each letter in my name, the string will be ______ cm long.

B. Write a fraction in words and a decimal number for each letter. Then write the correct amount of each letter in the boxes.

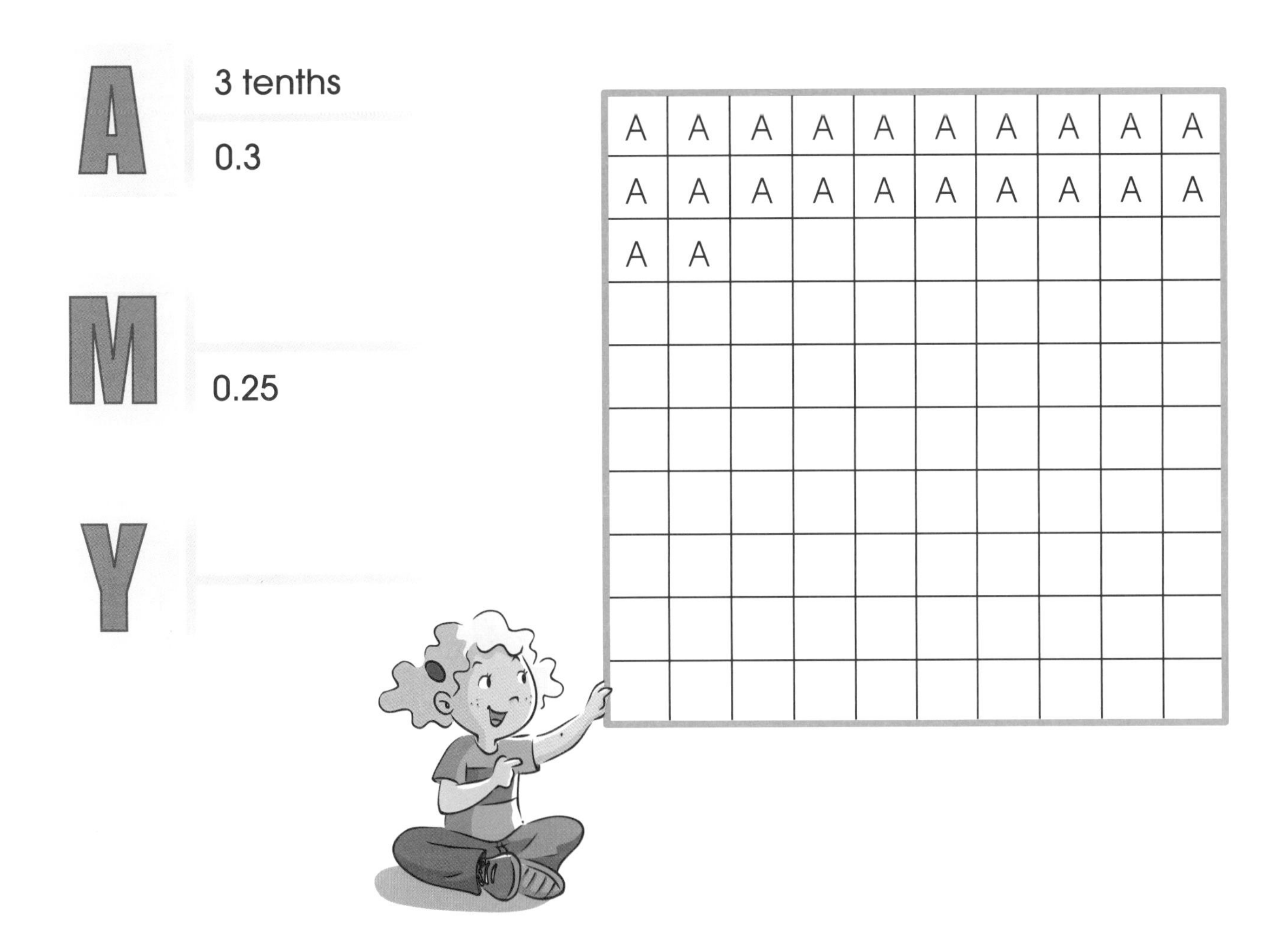

C. **Help Eli and Tony find the volume of each letter in their names. Then write two equivalent fractions to show how much of each letter is coloured.**

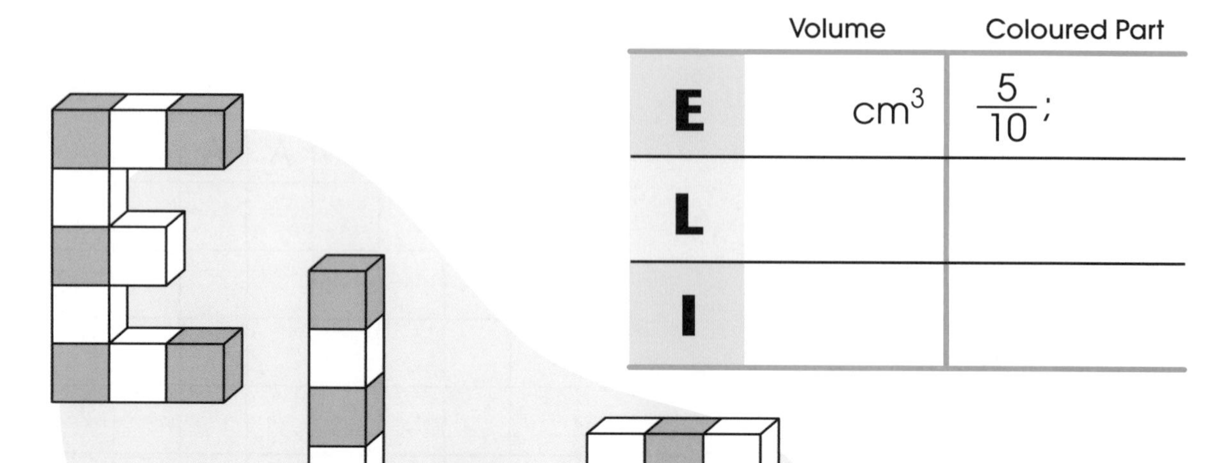

	Volume	Coloured Part
E	cm^3	$\frac{5}{10}$;
L		
I		

	Volume	Coloured Part
T		
O		
N		
Y		

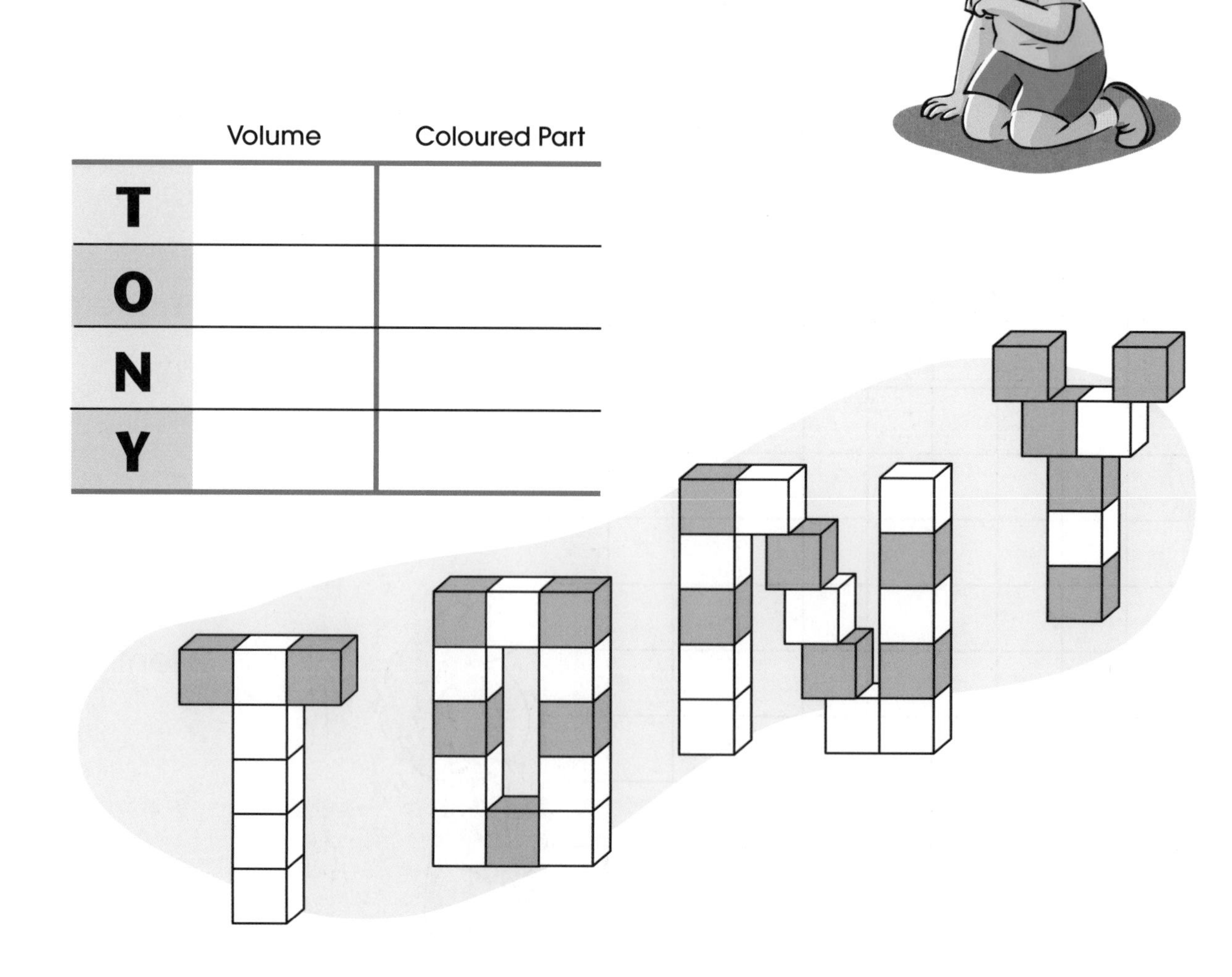

D. Measure the marked angle of each letter. Then redraw the letters with the same angles.

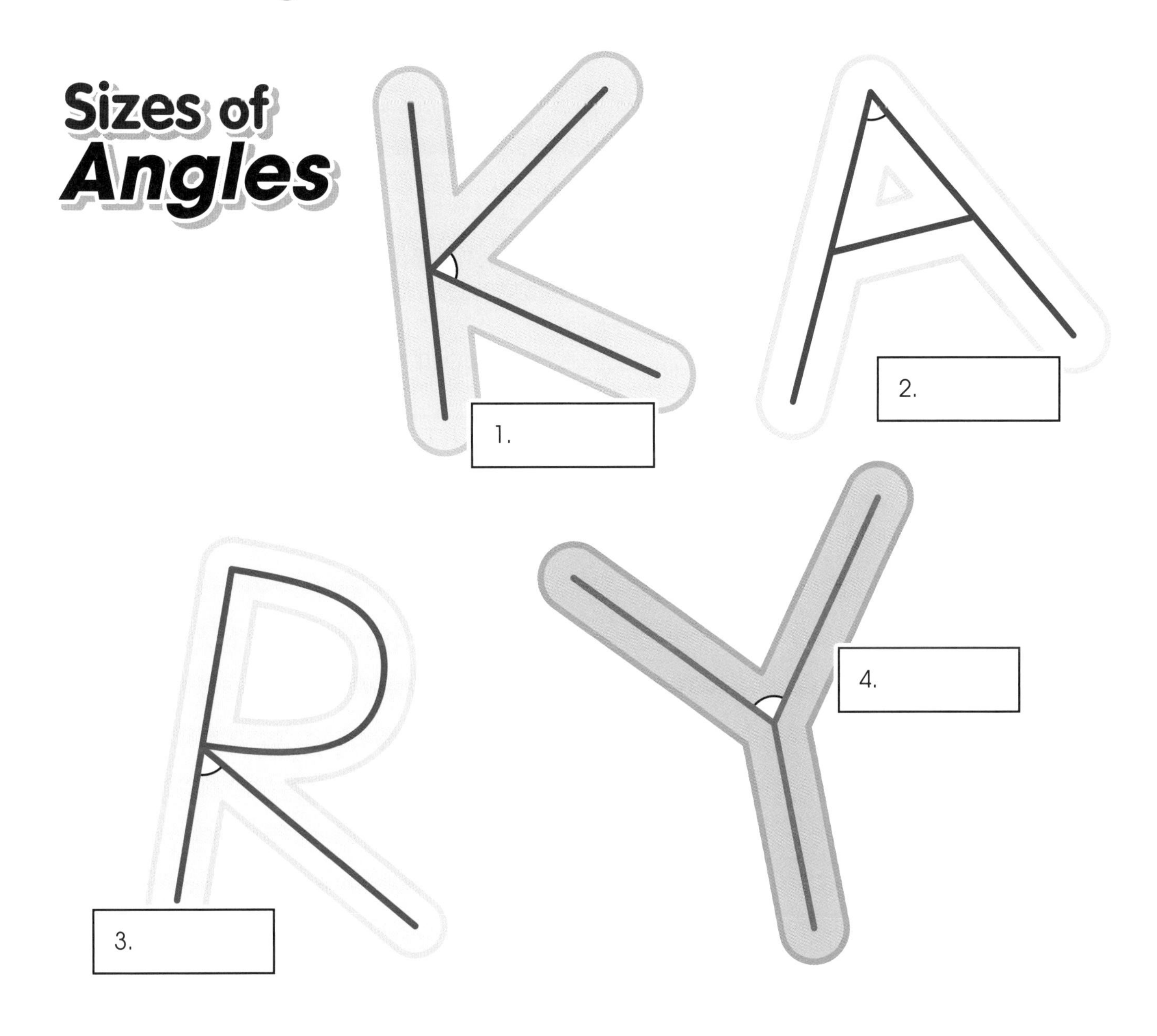

Look at the organs in the human body. Write the organs that belong to the systems. Then circle the correct words that describe the organs and the systems.

Digestive System

organ

s__________ : digests the food you eat with gastric / lemon juice

s__________ i__________ : about 4.5 m / 45 cm long

r__________ : the last section of the heart / large intestine

function

- processes the food that you throw / eat
- breaks the food down into the nutrients / oxygen that your body needs to live and grow
- waste materials are removed / absorbed from your body after digestion

Respiratory System

organ

l__________ : the right lung has 2 / 3 lobes and the left lung has 2 / 3 lobes

function

- brings air / food into your body
- allows your body to take in oxygen / carbon dioxide and removes oxygen / carbon dioxide

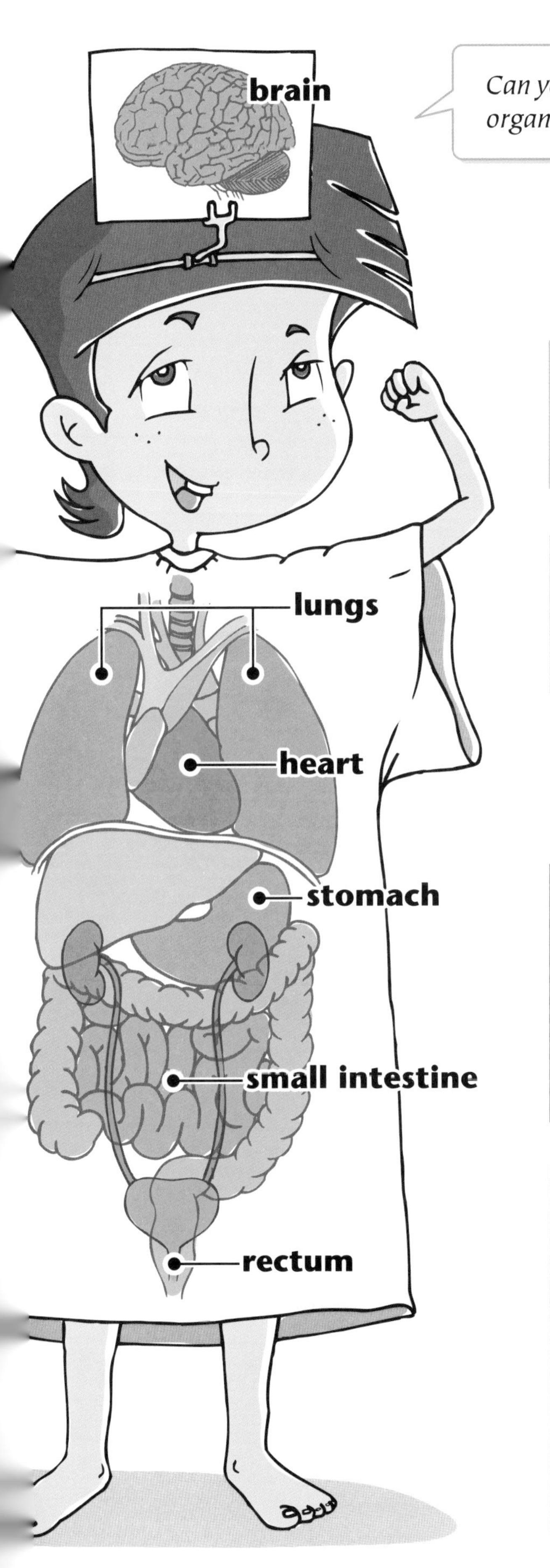

Can you identify all of the organs in your body?

Circulatory System

organ	h________ : size of a bean / fist
function	• pumps blood / messages to every part of your body

Nervous System

organ	b________ : a soft / hard organ that weighs about 1.5 kg / 20 kg
function	• is made up of the brain, the spinal cord, and bones / nerves • sends, receives, and processes nerve impulses throughout the body / spine

A. Fill in the blanks to learn about children's rights.

The United Nations' Convention on the Rights of the Child sets out the rights of children under 18 years of age. Below are some of those rights.

Convention on the Rights of the Child

opinion
education
religion
parents name
needs play

The right to:
My name is...
a 1. ________ and a nationality

The right to:
live with and be raised by their 2. ________

The right to:
have their basic 3. ________ fulfilled

The right to:
I think that...
voice their 4. ________

The right to:
a good quality 5. ________

The right to:
practise their 6. ________

The right to:
7. ________ and rest

B. Fill in the blanks to complete the sentences. Then write the letters under the correct headings.

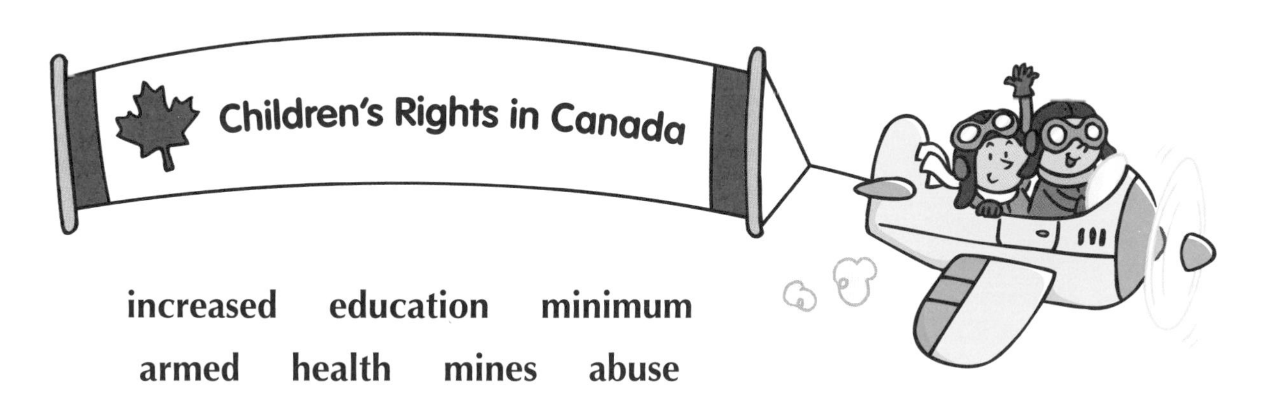

The Canadian Charter of Rights and Freedoms

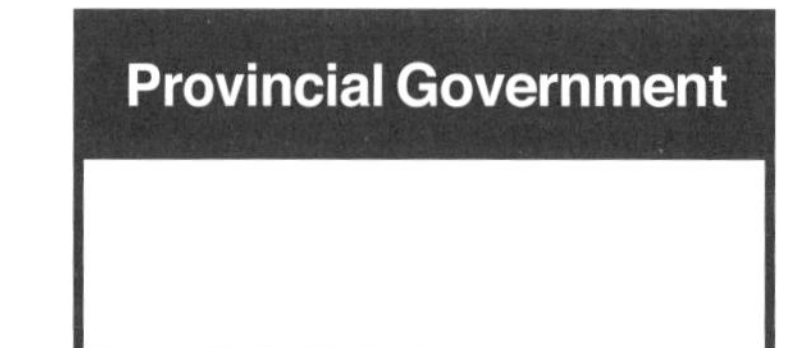

A. There are universal ________________ insurance plans that cover all children.

B. Canadian soldiers under 18 are prohibited from being deployed in ________________ conflict.

C. The ________________ age for employment is 14 in Ontario.

D. Many criminal laws are designed to prevent child ________________ .

E. Children have the right to receive ________________ in English and French.

F. The maximum punishments for those who violate the laws against child abuse have been greatly ________________ .

G. In Ontario, it is against the law to employ children under 16 to work in ________________ .

English

- read a passage and write questions
- write a newspaper article
- write synonyms, antonyms, and homophones
- rewrite sentences using correct punctuation and capitalization

Mathematics

- calculate distances and time lapses
- interpret fractions and decimals written in words
- solve problems involving subtraction and division
- complete patterns

Science

- review what matter is
- explore the properties of matter

Social Studies

- learn about Canada's international aid criteria and themes
- learn about Canada's support in providing international aid

Week 6 English

A. Read the passage about Linda's safari adventure. Then write "T" for the true sentences and "F" for the false ones.

Linda has just returned from a five-week safari adventure in Africa and is going to share her safari experience with you.

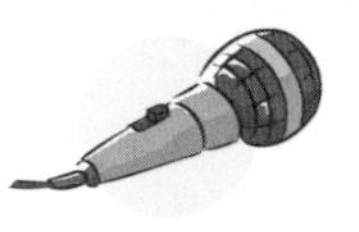

Were there any special preparations before your trip?

The medical preparation was of paramount importance. I took a TB skin test, several vaccines, and anti-malaria medication. I also needed a passport. In addition, I purchased neutral-coloured and breathable clothing, a mosquito bed net, insect repellent, and leather hiking boots to protect against possible snakebites. I brought along binoculars and a camera, too.

Which parts of Africa did you see on your safari adventure?

I saw parts of southern Africa, including South Africa, Namibia, Botswana, and Zimbabwe.

What were your favourite animals to see?

I was intrigued with the elephants in Zimbabwe. Their ritual of mourning the death of family members reminds me so much of human behaviour. They gather together, stroke the body with their trunks, and cover it with clumps of soil and grass.

Were there any times that you feared for your life?

The most frightening experience that I had was probably while staying on a game reserve in a savannah in Botswana. I noticed that my tent had a large tear that had been repaired. After inquiring about it, I found out that the night before, a lion had attempted to get into the tent. The camp manager assured me that safety precautions had been taken. They gave me a whistle and a horn. I was instructed to sound the horn in case of a medical emergency and the whistle for any animal threat. That night I didn't sleep at all.

1. Linda had a TB skin test after her adventure. ________
2. Zimbabwe is part of southern Africa. ________
3. Linda stayed on a game reserve in Botswana. ________
4. She was almost killed by an elephant at night. ________
5. She repaired a tear on her tent by herself. ________

B. Write four more questions to ask Linda so that you can learn more about her adventure.

- ______________________________
- ______________________________
- ______________________________
- ______________________________

C. **Write an article for the local paper summarizing the highlights of Linda's trip. Use the interview information from (A) to help you.**

headline

SUNDAY NEWS

body

Week 6

English

D. Use the clues to write the words. Draw yourself in the circle and use the letters in the coloured boxes to answer the question. Then rewrite the sentences with the correct punctuation and capitalization.

Synonyms

words that have the same meaning

1. courageous: _ _ _ _ _
2. sick: _ _ _
3. cautious: _ _ _ _ _ _ _
4. holiday: _ _ _ _ _ _ _ _

Antonyms

words that have opposite meanings

5. lost: _ _ _ _ _
6. weak: _ _ _ _ _ _
7. shout: _ _ _ _ _ _ _
8. vanish: _ _ _ _ _ _

Homophones

words that sound the same but are spelled differently

9. flower: _ _ _ _ _
10. paws: _ _ _ _ _
11. muscle: _ _ _ _ _ _
12. plane: _ _ _ _ _
13. seen: _ _ _ _ _

It is _ _ _ _ _ _ _ _ (1 2 3 4 5 6 7 8)
_ _ _ _ _ . (9 10 11 12 13)

14. victoria falls is a popular tourist attraction

____

____

15. victoria falls is located in southern africa

____

____

A. Look at the picture. Write a decimal to show how far away each place is from Amy's house. Then solve the problems.

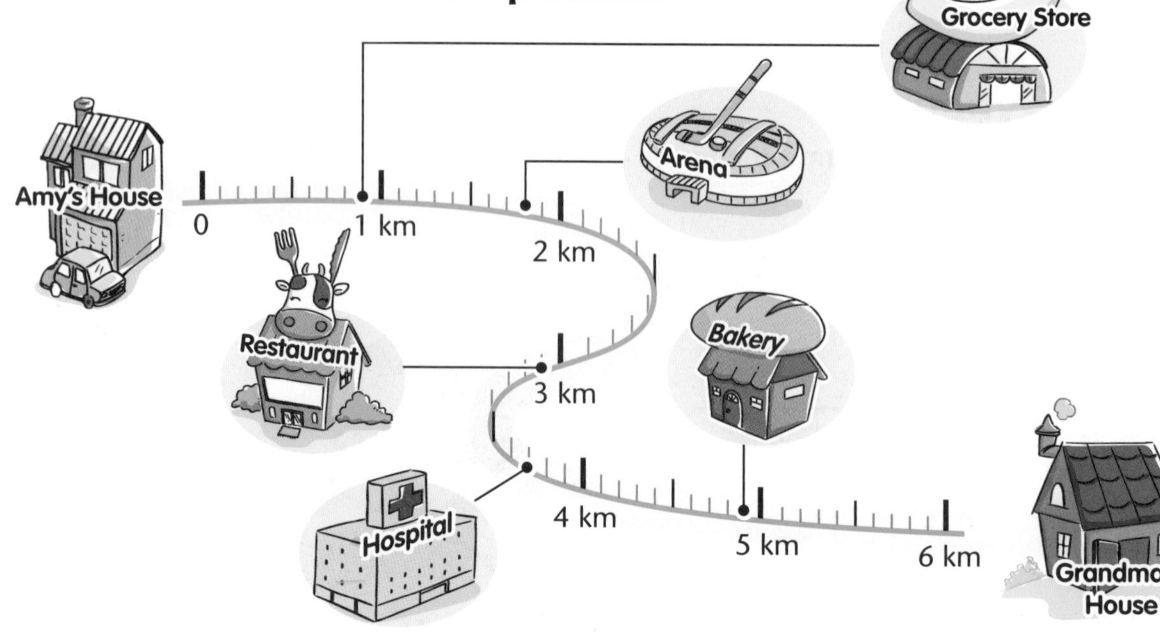

1. Distance from Amy's house to the
   - grocery store: ________
   - arena: ________
   - restaurant: ________
   - hospital: ________
   - bakery: ________

2. Distance from Grandma's house to the
   - bakery: ________
   - hospital: ________
   - restaurant: ________
   - arena: ________
   - grocery store: ________

3. How long did it take for Amy's family to travel from their house to Grandma's house?

   ____

4. How many metres did Amy's family travel in 1 minute?

   ____

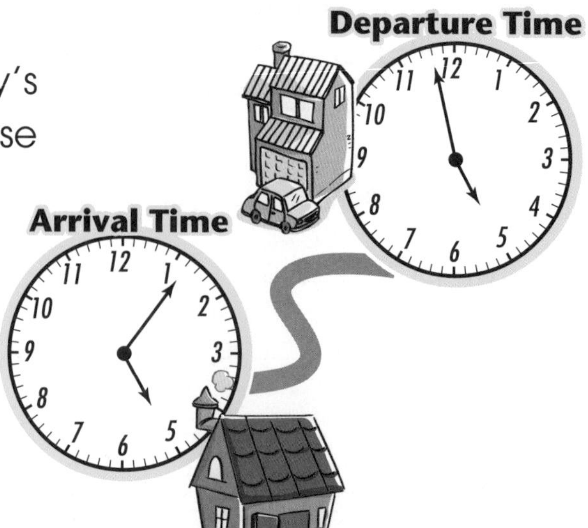

Week 6

Mathematics

B. Check the correct pictures.

1. $\frac{1}{2}$ of the fruit are apples:

2. $1\frac{1}{4}$ boxes of muffins have chocolate chips:

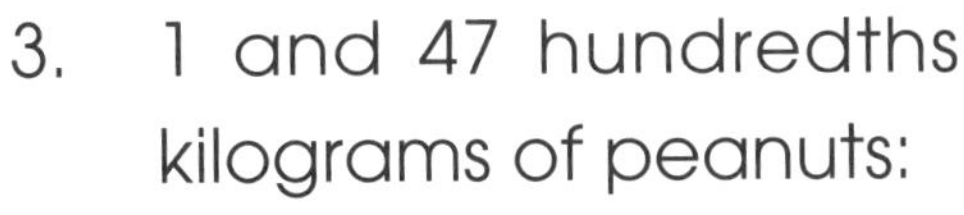

3. 1 and 47 hundredths kilograms of peanuts:

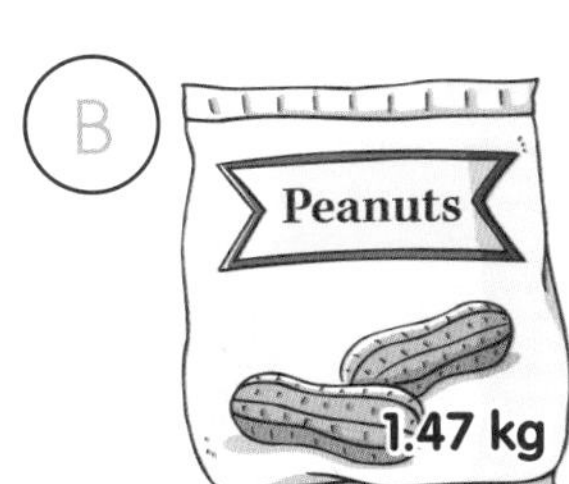

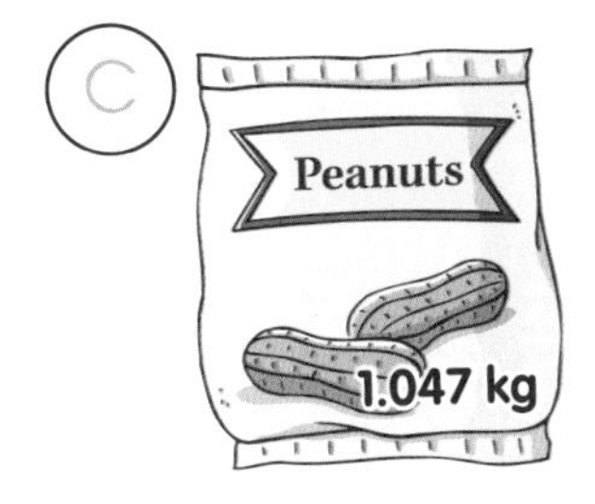

4. 2 tenths and 4 hundredths kilograms of sunflower seeds:

C. Amy measured the weight of the uneaten food in each container. Record how much food is left and how much was eaten. Then answer the questions with fractions.

1.

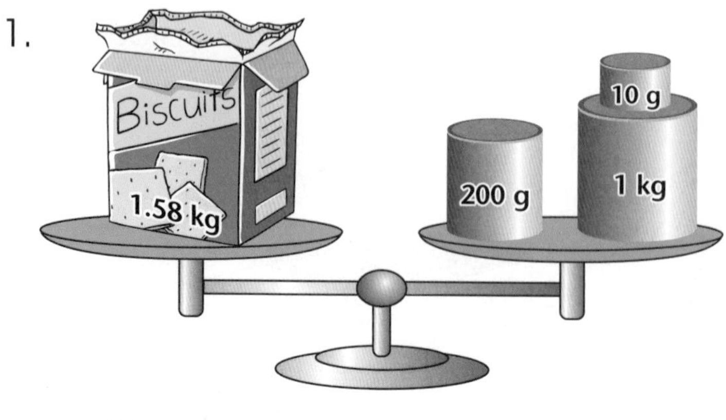

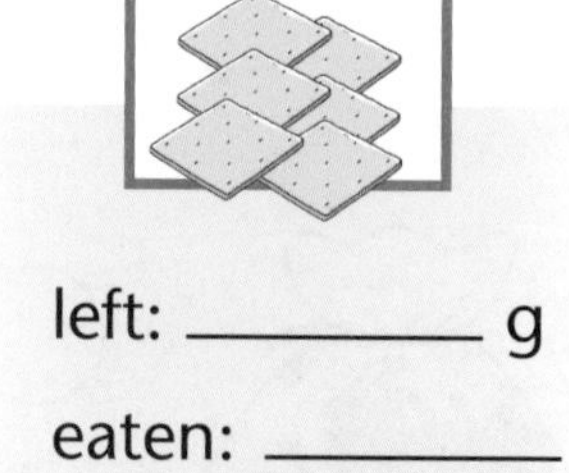

left: ________ g

eaten: ________

left: ________

eaten: ________

left: ________

eaten: ________

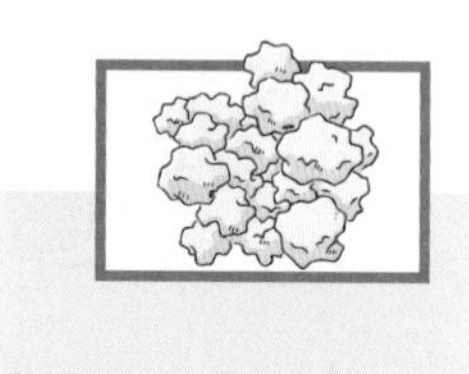

2. If Amy divides 33 pieces of biscuits into 6 groups, there will be ________ pieces of biscuits in 1 group.

3. If Amy and her sister share 391 grams of popcorn with their parents, each of them will get ________ grams of popcorn.

4. If my sister and I share 26 cookies with 2 cousins, each of us will get ________ cookies.

D. Look at the needlework. Draw x's from the line(s) of symmetry in each patch to complete the pattern.

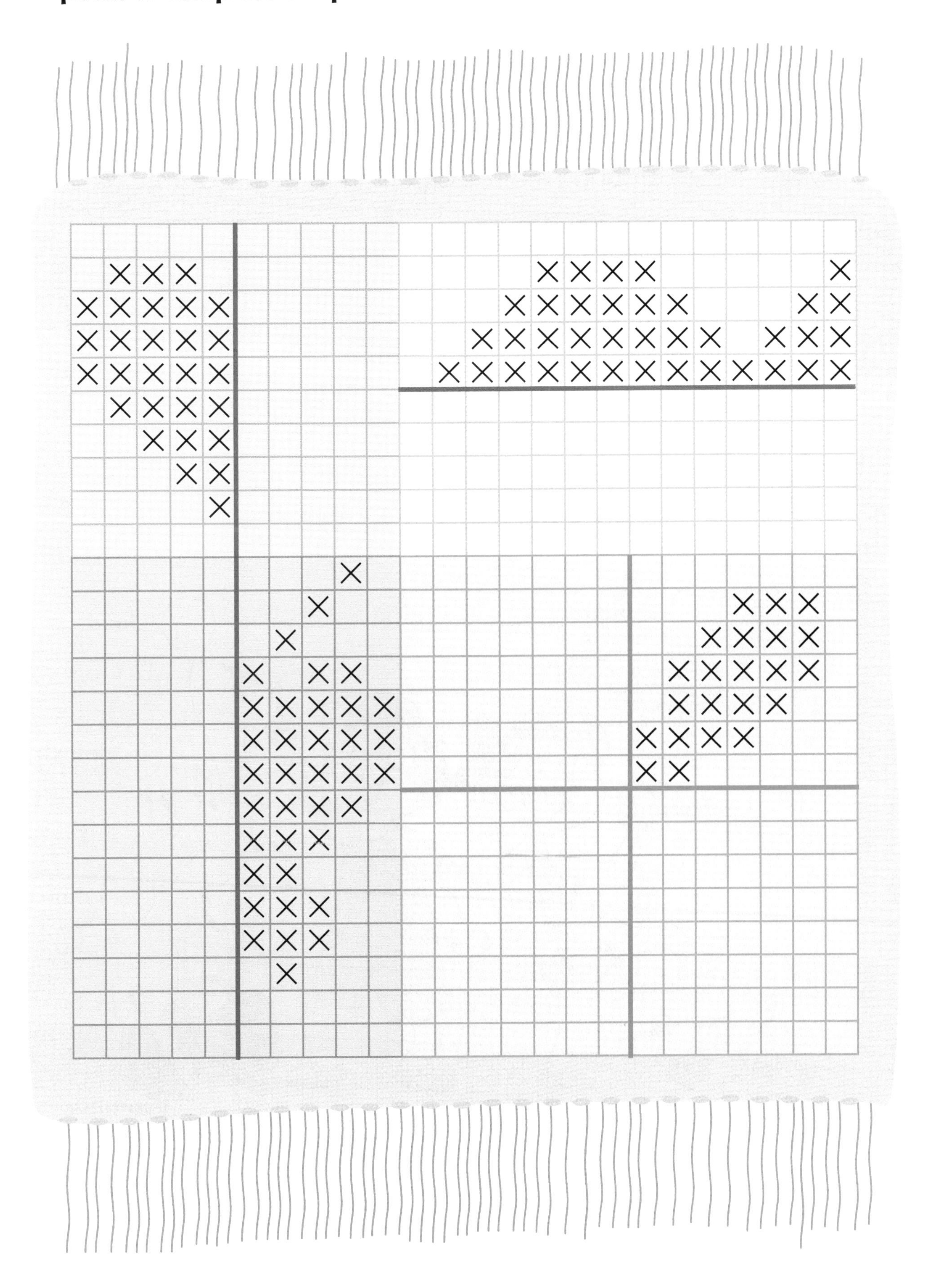

Week 6 Science

A. Fill in the blanks to complete the description of matter. Then check the things that are matter.

What Is Matter?

Many things around us are matter. In fact, we are 1. ____________ (inorganic/matter) too. Matter is anything that takes up 2. ____________ (space/tasks), which means it has 3. ____________ (boxes/volume). It also has 4. ____________ (weight/smell), which means it can be measured on a 5. ____________ (scale/ruler).

Things That Are Matter:

B. Match the descriptions with the words. Then circle the correct words to describe the properties of each thing.

Properties of *Matter*

viscosity clarity lustre texture solubility hardness malleability

1. ______ : the resistance of a substance to flow
2. ______ : the resistance of a substance to change shape
3. ______ : the capacity of being shaped
4. ______ : the clearness of a substance
5. ______ : the way the surface of a substance looks and feels
6. ______ : the ability of a substance to dissolve
7. ______ : the ability of a substance to reflect light

8.

honey

- viscosity: high / low
- clarity: opaque / translucent

the blade of a knife

- clarity: transparent / opaque
- lustre: dull / shiny

chopping board

- hardness: high / low
- texture: rough / smooth

sugar

- solubility: high / low
- lustre: dull / shiny

A. **Answer the girl's question. Then draw lines to match the themes with the descriptions.**

Canada's International Aid

Canada helps other countries based on the three criteria listed below. Which one do you think is the most important determiner? Put a check mark in the box and explain your choice.

Three criteria for selecting countries:

- ☐ needs
- ☐ ability to benefit meaningfully from Canada's aid
- ☐ alignment with Canada's foreign policy

Reason for Your Choice ______________________________

____

Three themes Canada's support is focused on:

Theme	Description
increasing food security	• access to quality basic education
securing the future of children and youth	• growing small and medium-sized businesses
stimulating sustainable economic growth	• child survival including maternal, newborn, and child health
	• sustainable agricultural development
	• investing in people by increasing access to skill training and increasing learning opportunities
	• food assistance and nutrition

Week 6 Social Studies

B. Complete the reports to learn about how Canada provided aid and support to other countries.

RCMP relief medical search

Earthquake in Haiti

Date: January 12, 2010
Magnitude: 7.0 on the Richter Scale

The earthquake claimed thousands of lives. It destroyed Port-au-Prince, the capital of Haiti. Buildings, including hospitals and schools, were ruined. The destruction of the communication systems made it hard to locate survivors and dispatch rescue teams.

Canada's Rescue Efforts:

- sent expert personnel from the ____________ and the Canadian Forces to provide security services, help ____________ and rescue, give ____________ care, and distribute food and water
- committed to providing $550 million in aid and humanitarian ____________

donations food treatment contributed

Food and Nutrition Crisis in the Sahel, West Africa

Year: 2012

The crisis arose due to long periods of drought, scattered rain, poor harvest, and the resulting high food prices. It is estimated that 18.7 million people were affected and over a million children under five years old were dying from severe acute malnutrition.

Canada's Rescue Efforts:

- partnered with or supported various NGOs in providing ____________ and nutrition assistance and ____________ to children suffering from severe acute malnutrition
- launched the Sahel Crisis Matching Fund to match dollar-for-dollar the ____________ from Canadians
- ____________ about $57.5 million by the end of 2012 to help people affected by the crisis

English

- read three journal entries
- complete a crossword puzzle
- find and write alliterative phrases
- learn about sarcasm

Mathematics

- find information from a graph
- complete a table and solve problems
- identify the correct nets and find the areas

Science

- review the three states of matter
- identify changes in the states of matter

Social Studies

- learn about Canada's participation in resolving environmental issues
- learn about invasive species in Canada

* The Canadian penny is no longer in circulation. It is used in the unit to show money amounts to the cent.

A. Read the journal entries.

Hillary's Horrendous Holiday

Monday, July 7

I was supposed to go away with my friend Laura to her family's luxurious cottage, but she got sick, so I am stuck going on another fun-filled camping trip with my parents and my "lovely" little brother Leo. The drive was most enjoyable – crammed in the back seat beside Leo, listening to tedious toddler tunes in a monotone. We finally arrived at the campsite near dusk. It was pouring rain, and we were really hungry. Mom and Dad had purchased this new tent, which was supposed to be easy to assemble. They were in way over their heads, and were trying to read paper instructions in the middle of a downpour. After what seemed like an eternity, the tent was standing somewhat upright. I could have done it in a snap. Dad finally tried to light the portable stove so we could eat. More bad news – he forgot to pack the fuel. Dinner consisted of cereal in the back seat of the car, where we could at least stay dry.

Tuesday, July 8

Well, at least the sun shone brightly today. Mom and Dad finished unpacking, while I was the entertainment committee for Leo. I am so exhausted from playing "Hide and Go Seek" and "Ring Around the Rosie". Later, I had some time to check out the facilities at the campsite. What facilities – there were none! No shower, no electricity, and no toilets – just offensively odoured outhouses. Mom said that tonight we would be going out for dinner. I was elated, but I found out afterwards that what she meant was we were eating outdoors. Mom tried to help with the barbecuing, but Dad's the real expert. Let's just say we had real charbroiled burgers.

Wednesday, July 9

Today, we drove to a beach. The fact that we were the only ones at the beach should have spoken volumes. The water was freezing, the beach was covered in seaweed, and there were swarms of deer flies. I knew this was as close to having a shower as I would get, so I braved the waters. When I got out, I was horrified to find two leeches latched onto my leg. Fortunately, Mom and Dad had a packet of salt in the car, which helped remove them. I wonder what exceptionally exciting experiences tomorrow will bring...

B. Read the clues and complete the crossword puzzle with words from the passage.

C. Find five alliterative phrases in Hillary's journal and write them on the lines below. Then make up your own alliterative phrases with the given letters.

Alliterative Phrases from Hillary's Journal:

Alliteration is when two or more words in a group of words begin with the same letter or sound.

An example of an alliterative phrase:

1. ____________________
2. ____________________
3. ____________________
4. ____________________
5. ____________________

My Alliterative Phrases

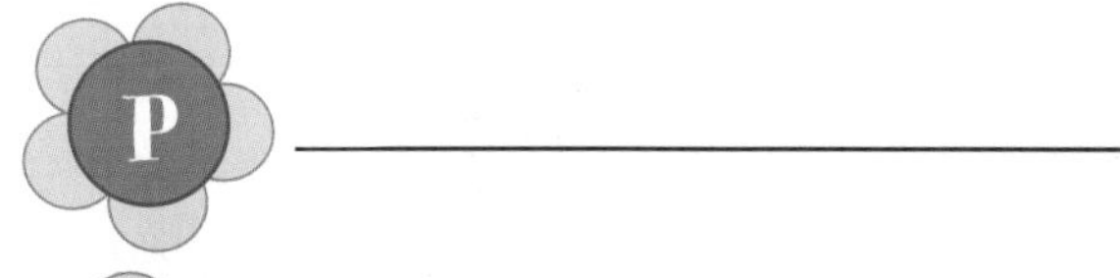

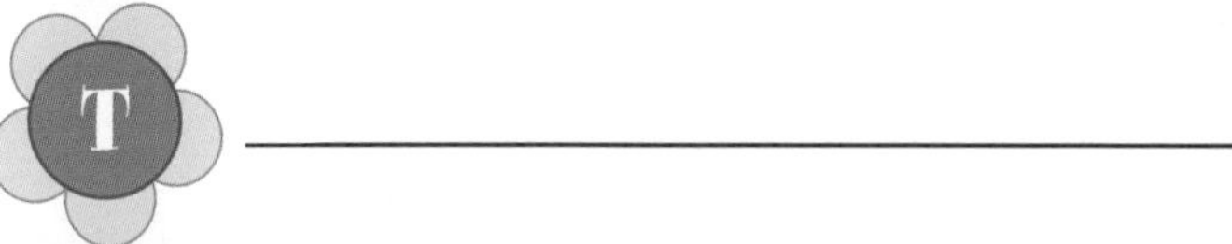

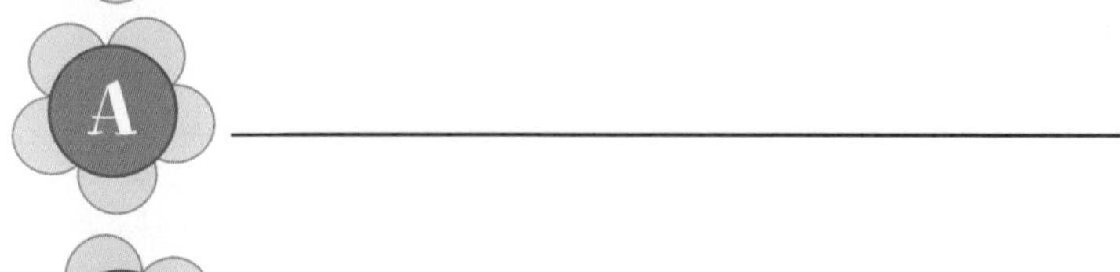

See if you can write alliterative phrases with four words or more.

D. Hillary used sarcasm* in her journal entries. Check the real meaning of Hillary's sentences.

* **Sarcasm** is language with a mocking tone that means the opposite of what is being said.

1. "The drive was most enjoyable."

   It really means:

   The drive was

   (A) exciting.

   (B) long.

   (C) unpleasant.

2. "Dad's the real experl."

   It really means:

   (A) Dad knows a lot.

   (B) Dad knows nothing about that area.

   (C) Dad's the worst cook.

3. "I wonder what exceptionally exciting experiences tomorrow will bring."

   It really means:

   (A) I wonder what bad things will happen tomorrow.

   (B) I wonder what time I will go home tomorrow.

   (C) I wonder what great things will happen tomorrow.

E. Rewrite these sentences using sarcasm.

1. This is the worst lemonade I have ever tasted.

   ____

2. He put me in a room so small that I could hardly lie straight.

   ____

A. **Read the graph that shows the sales at Joe's Bakery for the past nine months. Then fill in the information.**

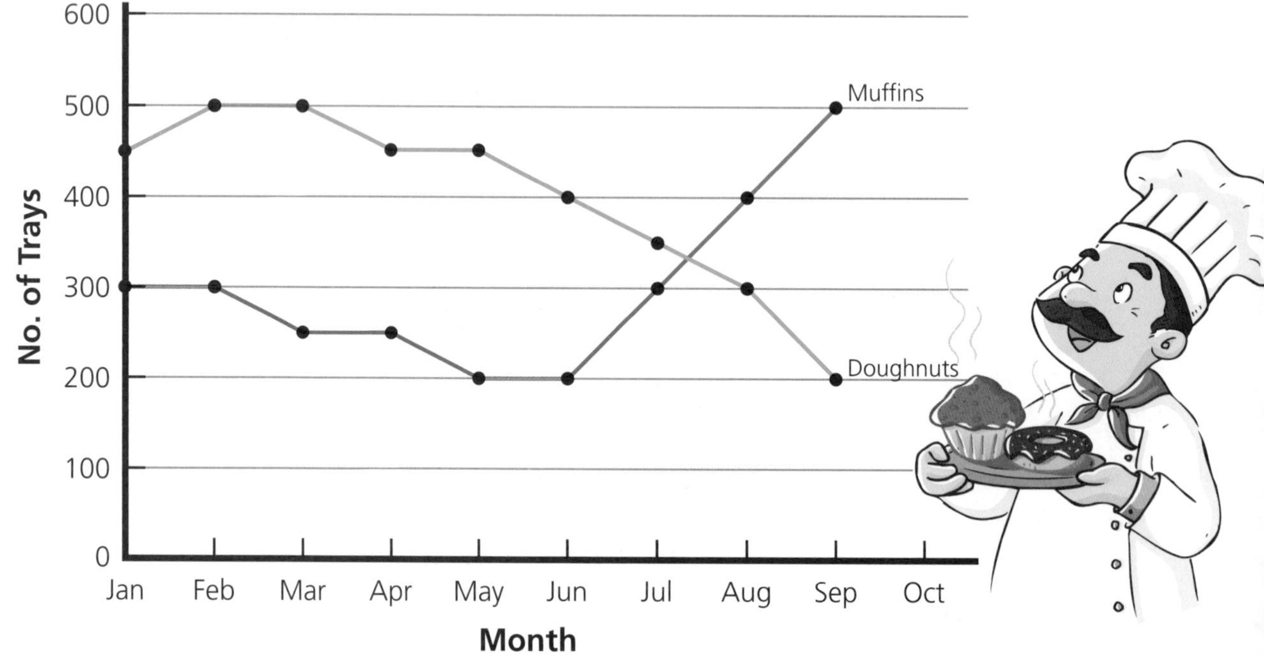

1.

a. No. of trays sold in April:

____

b. No. of months with over 250 trays sold:

____

c. The month with the most muffins sold:

____

2.

a. No. of trays sold in August:

____

b. No. of months with fewer than 300 trays sold:

____

c. The month with the fewest doughnuts sold:

____

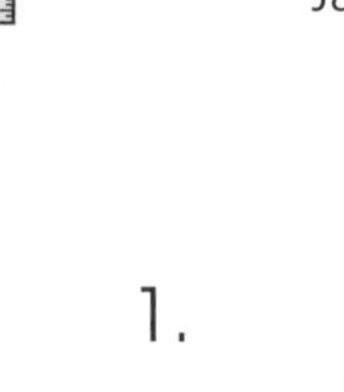

B. Look at the graph in (A) again. Answer Joe's questions.

1. *I introduced a popular new flavour of muffins a few months ago. In which month do you think I started selling those muffins. Why?*

Joe's Bakery

2. If the sales of muffins follow the trend, how many trays of muffins will be sold in October?

3. What was the average number of trays of doughnuts sold per month?

4. A famous doughnut shop opened next to my bakery a few months ago. In which month did it open? Why?

C. The muffins from Joe's Bakery are sold in three different boxes. Find the cost of one muffin in each box. Then complete the table and answer the questions.

1.

2.

No. of Boxes (Regular-sized)	No. of Muffins	Cost
1		
2		
3		
4		
5		

3. Mr. Kim wants to buy 10 muffins. Which boxes of muffins should he buy? How much will it cost?

____

4.

____

D. Joe is looking for boxes to hold doughnuts. Check the nets that can form boxes and put a cross for the ones that cannot. Then find the areas of the checked nets.

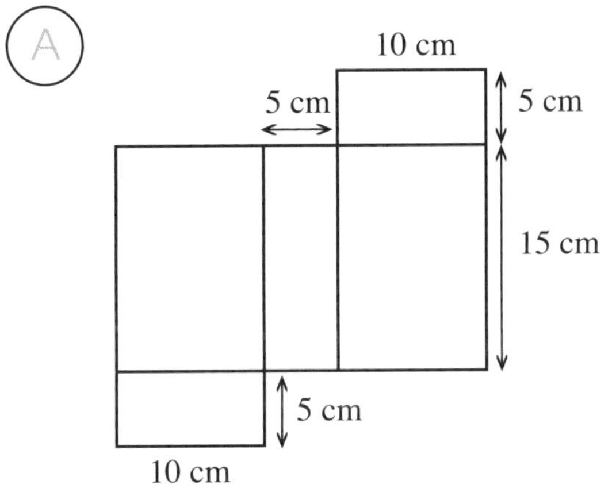

Boxes to Hold Doughnuts

A

10 cm
5 cm
5 cm
15 cm
5 cm
10 cm

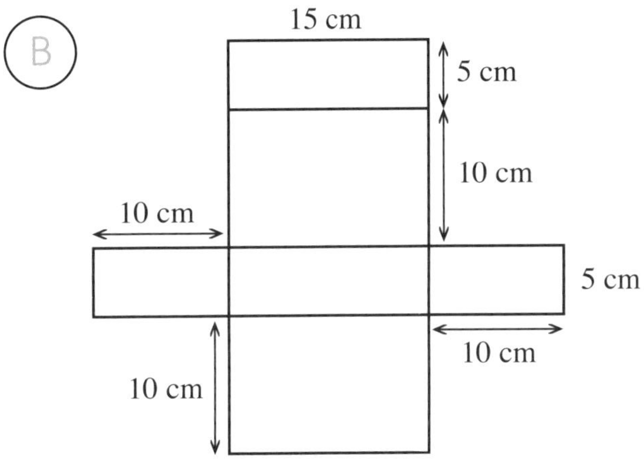

B

15 cm
5 cm
10 cm
10 cm
5 cm
10 cm
10 cm

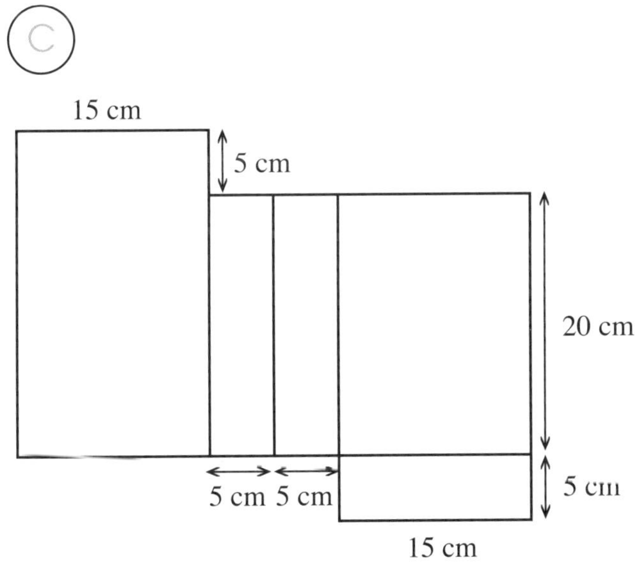

C

15 cm
5 cm
20 cm
5 cm 5 cm
5 cm
15 cm

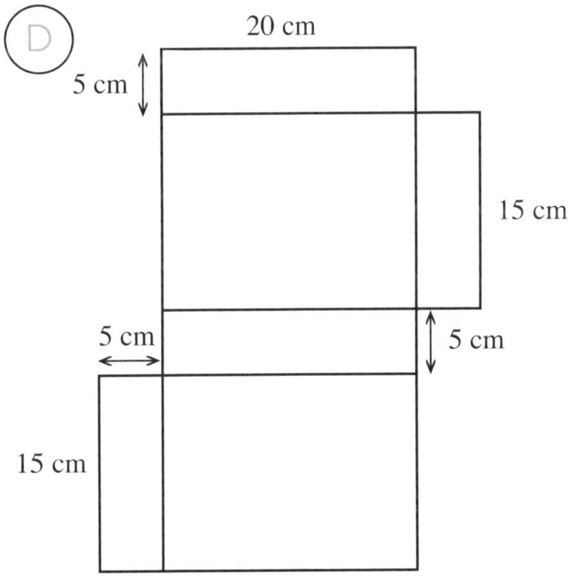

D

20 cm
5 cm
15 cm
5 cm
5 cm
15 cm

Area of Net ◯ :

__________ cm²

Area of Net ◯ :

__________ cm²

A. Identify the states of matter shown in the pictures. Then read the properties and write the states that match those properties.

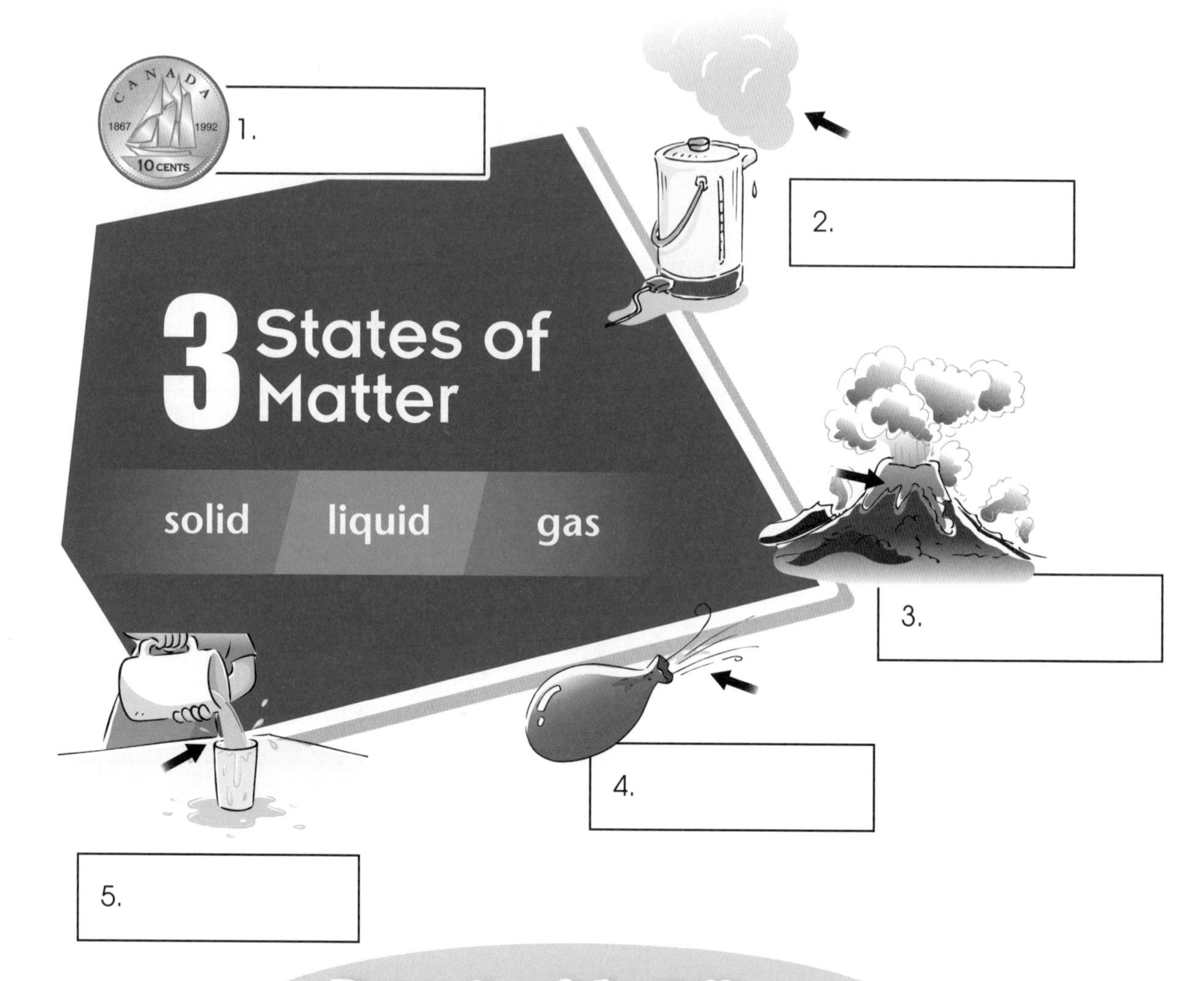

Properties of the Different States of Matter

6. ____________________

- definite shape
- definite volume
- cannot flow

7. ____________________

- no definite shape
- definite volume
- takes the shape of its container

8. ____________________

- no definite shape
- no definite volume
- fills its entire container regardless of its amount

B. Write the changes in the states of matter and determine whether heat is added or taken away during each change.

Changes in States

sublimation condensation freezing
melting evaporation

- added
- taken away

1.

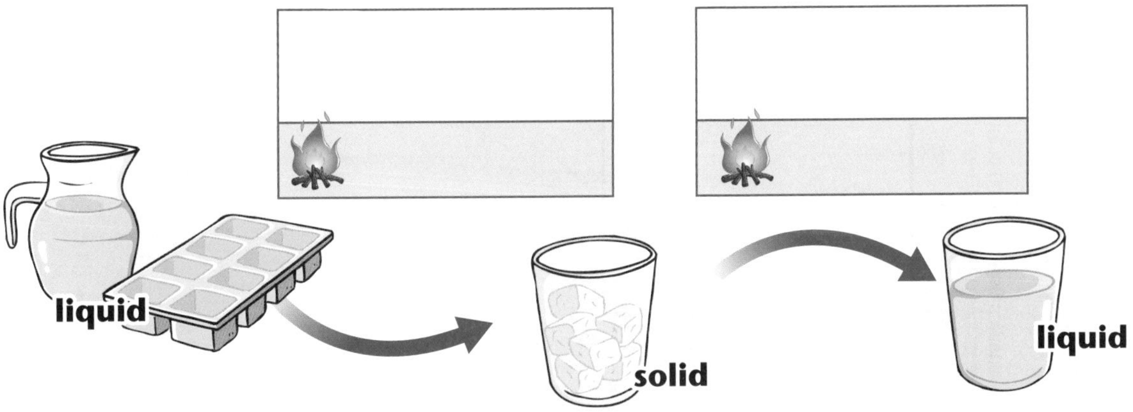

liquid

solid

liquid

2.

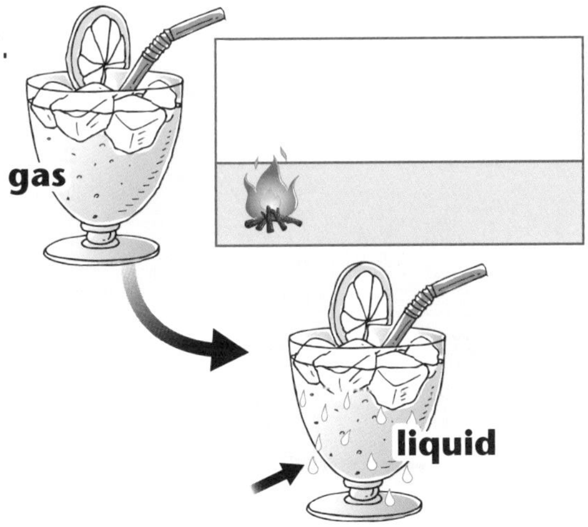

gas

liquid

3.

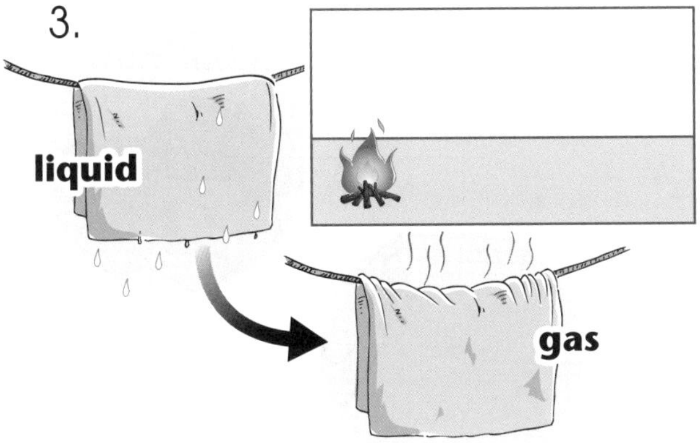

liquid

gas

4.

I put some moth balls in the closet six months ago and they have all disappeared.

change in state:

a. ______________________

heat:

b. ______________________

Week 7

Social Studies

A. Read the paragraph and study the graph. Then give short answers to the questions.

Canada has taken part in international actions toward resolving various environmental issues. An example is the Kyoto Protocol. It is an international agreement under the United Nations Framework Convention on Climate Change. Canada participated, with the target of reducing greenhouse gas emissions to 6% below its 1990 level over the period of 2008 – 2012.

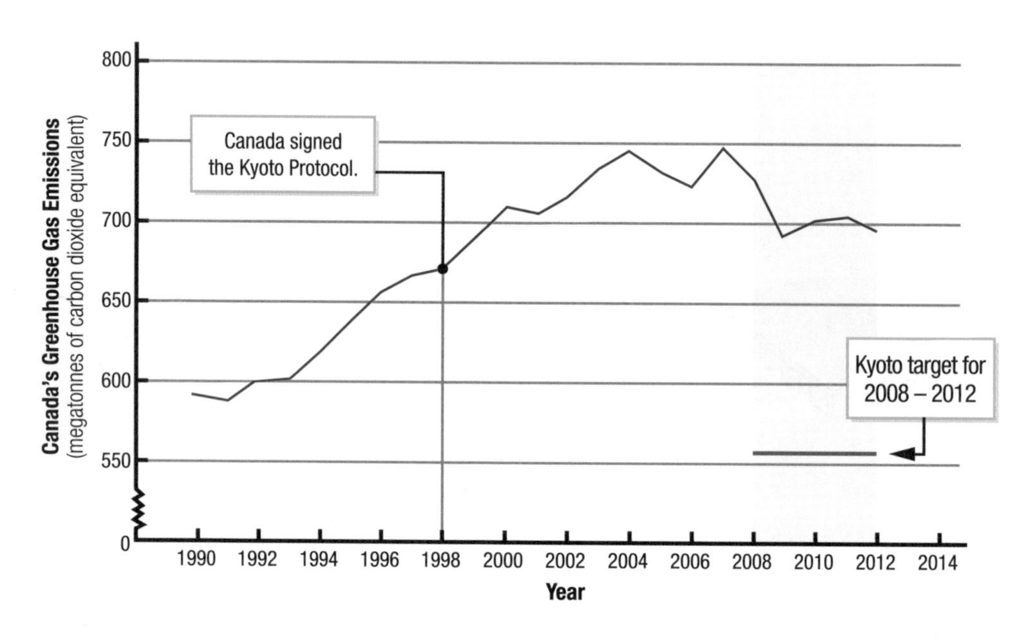

1. What environmental issue is the Kyoto Protocol targeted to resolve?

   ____

2. In what year did Canada sign the Kyoto Protocol?

   ____

3. In general, had Canada's greenhouse gas emissions been increasing or decreasing from 1990 to 2007?

   ____

4. Did Canada manage to meet the committed target?

   ____

Canada withdrew from the Kyoto Protocol in 2012, but continues to support other international efforts to combat global climate change.

B. Read what the boy says. Circle the correct words and answer the question.

Invasive species is another environmental issue that poses a threat to Canada. They are harmful non-native plant and animal species that threaten the local natural habitats, economy, society, and people's health. One such species is the zebra mussel.

Zebra Mussels

Introduction to Canada: intentional / unintentional

- came to **North / South** America in the late 1980s through ballast water discharged from cargo **trains / ships**

Areas Affected:

- Lake Erie, Lake St. Clair, and the Detroit River, all of which border both Canada and the **United States / Great Britain**

Major Impact:

- have wiped out native **mussels / birds** from the affected areas
- rapidly colonize on various surfaces, such as pipes, buoys, and fishing nets, thereby clogging or **polishing / sinking** them
- their feeding increases water clarity and light penetration, which results in an overgrowth of **terrestrial / aquatic** vegetation

Control Measure:

- making laws to ensure that all ships entering Canadian waters manage their ballast water in a responsible manner

Do you think Canada can resolve the environmental issues of greenhouse gas emissions and invasive species without collaborating with other countries? Why?

____

____

____

____

Arts and Crafts

- make gourd maracas

Comics

- Pearls and Toads

Fun Places to Go in Summer

- Horseback Riding in Nova Scotia

Gourd Maracas

Materials:

- dried beans
- craft paint
- X-acto knife
- aluminum foil
- masking tape
- paintbrush
- craft spray (sealant)
- 2 oblong-shaped gourds

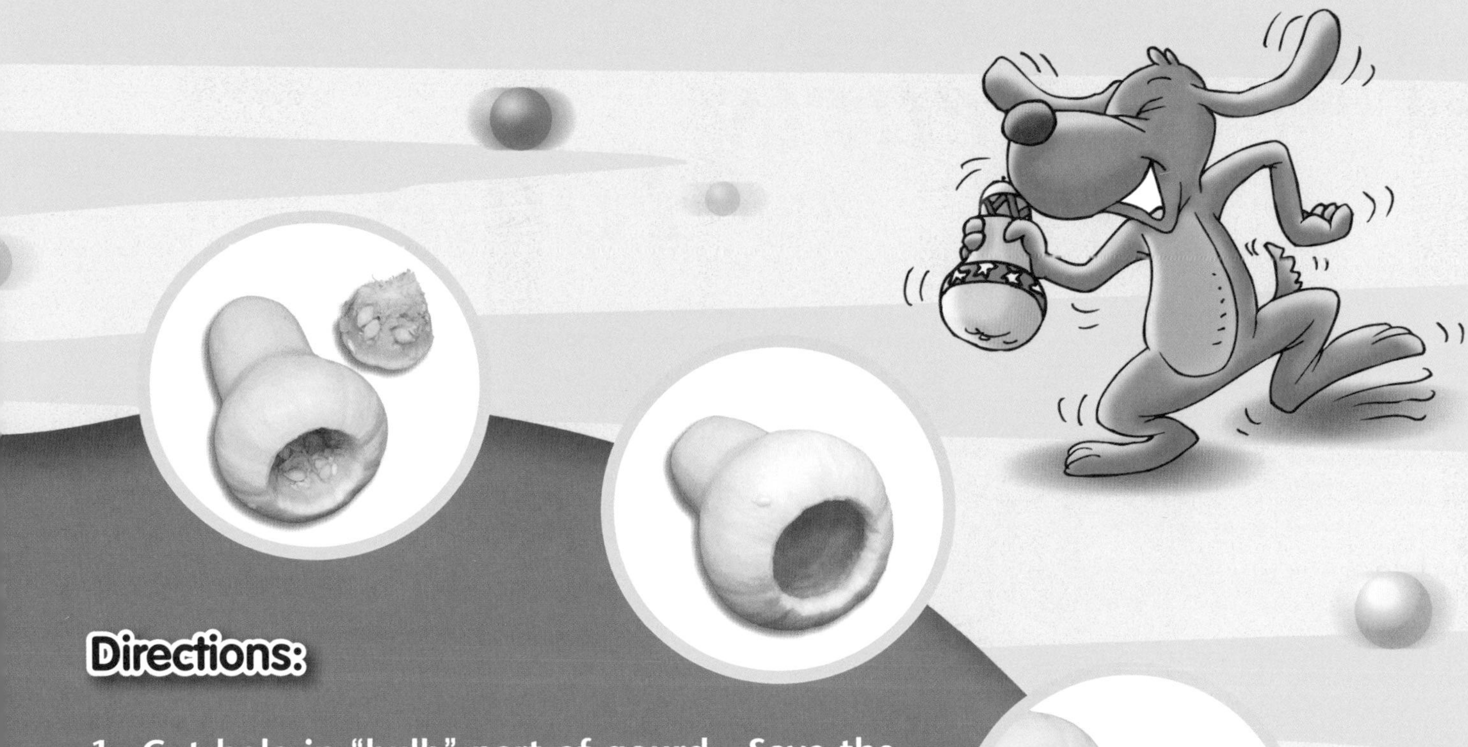

Directions:

1. Cut hole in "bulb" part of gourd. Save the cut-out piece.
2. Scoop out pulp. Let it dry overnight.
3. Pour 3 tablespoons of dried beans into gourd.
4. Cover the hole with aluminum foil.
5. Cover aluminum foil with the cut-out piece. Seal it with masking tape.
6. Paint gourd. Let it dry.
7. Spray gourd with craft spray (sealant).

Pearls and Toads

Once there was a young girl. She lived with her mother and her elder sister. The sister was the mother's favourite. They were both lazy and always angry.

Every day, the younger daughter walked a long way to fetch water from the well.

One day, there was an old woman sitting by the well.

"I would be happy to," said the girl. She filled her jug and gave it to the woman.

The girl did not know what to do. She quickly ran home and explained what had happened to her mother and sister. As she spoke, pearls dropped from her mouth and rolled on the floor.

Tomorrow, you'll go to the well. The fairy will surely give you a better gift.
So the next day, the older daughter went to the well.

A rich woman by the well asked the girl for a drink of water.
Get it yourself!
"She's not the fairy I'm looking for," thought the girl.
You're a rude and selfish girl. Your gift will be very different from your sister's.

The girl was very sad. She tried to tell her mother what happened but toads and snakes filled her mouth.

The mother was furious. She blamed everything on the younger daughter.

Horseback Riding in Nova Scotia

If you like interacting with animals and being in nature, a great way to combine both experiences is to go horseback riding in beautiful Nova Scotia on a fresh summer afternoon.

Learning to ride a horse is easy and fun, even if you've never done it before. Just follow your friendly guides' instructions – they will teach you the proper way to sit on a horse, how to hold the reigns, and how to direct your horse's movements. Then, hop in the saddle and get ready to explore the trails. You can ride at a leisurely canter while you soak up the beauty of the landscape, or urge your horse to gallop and feel the wind blow into your face as you spring forward.

You can take a riding tour of almost any part of Nova Scotia: explore grassy woodlands and pasturelands or ride along winding rivers. Some rides even give you a view of the famous Bay of Fundy!

When your ride is over, make sure to thank your new animal friend with some tasty treats!

Answers

Grades 5-6

Credits

Photos ("children" Gennadiy Poznyakov/123RF.com, "beach" Alexandr Ozerov/123RF.com)

Week 1

English

B. Fact: A ; C ; E ; F
Opinion: B ; D

C. (Suggested answers)
1. extremely
2. presented
3. gloomy
4. things
5. gone beyond

D. 1. werewolves
2. lives
3. benches
4. dormitories
5. alleys
6. classes
7. dreams
8. industries
9. countries
10. reviews

E. (Individual questions)

F. 1. groan
2. aloud
3. through
4. stare
5. coarse
6. mourning
7. whether
8. band

Mathematics

A. 1. 14.6 ; 30° ; 75° ; 75° ; isosceles
2. 10.41 ; 35° ; 90° ; 55° ; scalene
3. 8.55 ; 60° ; 60° ; 60° ; equilateral

B. 1. 0.05 ; 0.2 ; 0.3 ; 0.45 ; 0.55 ; 0.7 ; 0.8 ; 0.95
2. 0.15 m
3. 0.35 m
4. 4
5. Every 2 neighbouring flowers are 0.15 m apart and then 0.1 m apart alternately.

C. (Suggested answers)
1. $\frac{12}{16}$; $\frac{3}{4}$
2. $\frac{8}{20}$; $\frac{2}{5}$
3. $\frac{16}{24}$; $\frac{2}{3}$

D. 1.

$\frac{1}{2}$

2.

$\frac{3}{4}$

3.

$\frac{1}{2}$

E. 1. 96
2. 230
3. 432
4. 410
5. 425
6. 128.25

Science

A. coal ; C
solar energy ; G
wind ; F
water ; E
nuclear ; D
oil ; A
biomass ; B

B. 1. natural ; never
cannot ; limited
2a. wind ; renewable
b. coal ; non-renewable energy source
c. solar energy ; renewable energy source
d. biomass ; renewable energy source

Social Studies

A. 1.

2.

3.

4.

5.

B. Colour: 1, 3, 4
C. (Individual drawing and writing)

Week 2

English

B. These became the first roller coasters.
Many riders were injured.
Amusement parks became popular.
They had no money for leisure activities.
Theme parks were opening again and different roller coasters were created.

C. 1. developed 2. one hundred years
3. importance 4. upward motion

D. 1. The cost of building just one roller coaster is well into millions of dollars.
2. Cedar Point and Six Flags Magic Mountain are among the leading roller coaster amusement parks in the world.
3. Standing over 30 storeys high, "The Supreme Scream" is one of the world's tallest free fall rides.
4. One of the scientific principles behind how roller coasters move is based on gravity, which was discovered by Sir Isaac Newton.

E. (Sugesster answers)
1. Many people enjoy riding on roller coasters because they derive a lot of excitement from the rides.
2. When the Great Depression struck in 1929, the amusement park industry had to close down.

F. 1. C 2. B
3. B 4. B

G. (Individual writing)

Mathematics

A. 1. Sun: 3.40 ; 3 ; 40
Mon: 5.70 ; 5 and 70 hundredths
Tue: 1.90 ; 1 and 90 hundredths
Wed: 5.10 ; 5 and 10 hundredths
Thu: 0.60 ; 60 hundredths
Fri: 4.20 ; 4 and 20 hundredths
Sat: 6.80 ; 6 and 80 hundredths

2a. $10.20
b. $17.50
c. $27.70
3. 5

B. 1. 472.03
2. 179.60
3.

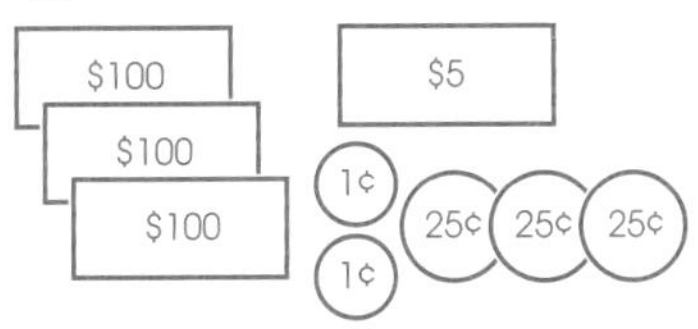

4.

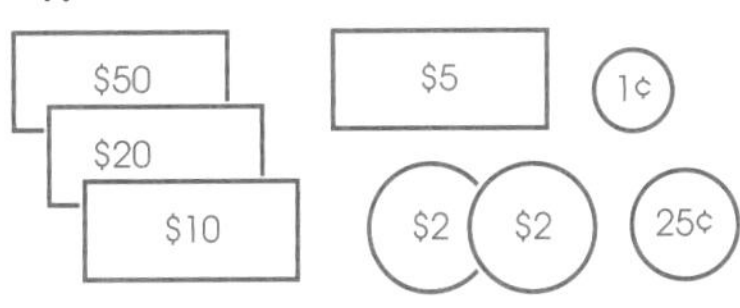

5. camera ; necklace
6. $382.77
7. $89.80

C. 1a. $\frac{7}{12}$
b. $\frac{4}{12}$ $(\frac{1}{3})$
c. $\frac{1}{12}$
d. $\frac{5}{12}$

2a. $84.66
b. $40 off

D. 1a.

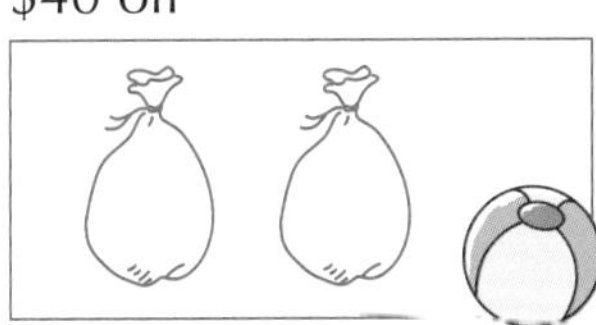

2

b.

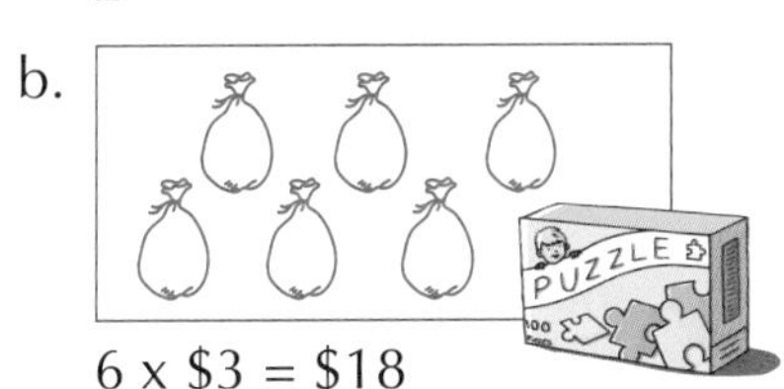

6 x $3 = $18

2a.

2

b. 

4 x $6 = $24

3. Darren: 10 ; 14 ; 8
   Eva: 5 ; 7 ; 4

Science

A. 1. external ; live load ; dead load

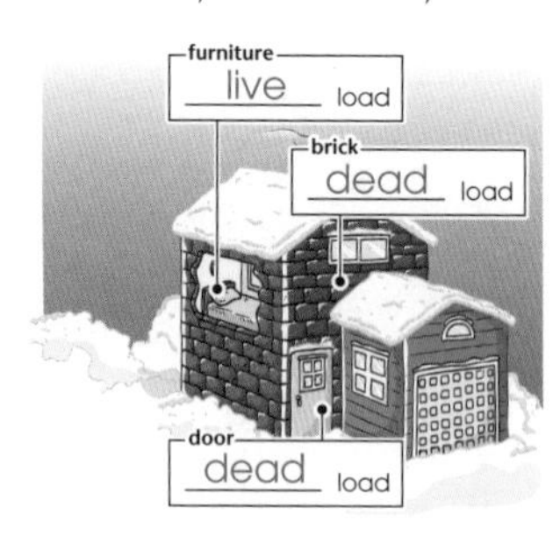

2. internal ; compression ; tension

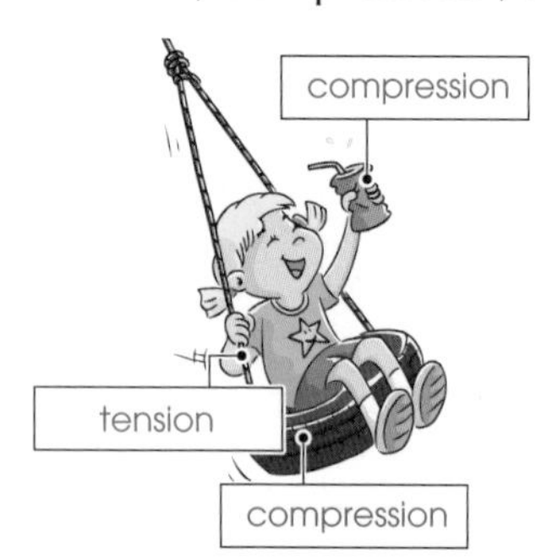

B. 1a. flexible　b. crisscrossing
   c. steel
   2a. drainage　b. higher
   c. masts
   3a. shutters　b. inward
   c. roof

Social Studies

A. 1. French
   2. Black Loyalists
   3. Irish
   4. countries

B. 1. poor ; adopted
   2. 1850s ; gold ; job
   3. fishermen ; camps ; federal

Week 3

English

A.

Dear Mom and Dad,

¶Adriana and I are having a fantastic time at Uncle Ross and Aunt Joyce's. It is like paradise here, with a view overlooking the water called "Satellite Channel" (not the television kind, Dad).¶I'm learning to really appreciate wildlife and the outdoors. Yesterday, while on the charter plane from Vancouver to Victoria, we were amazed to spot a pod of approximately 20 orcas, with their dorsal fins piercing through the water each time they surfaced. It was an incredible sight! Did you know that pods of the resident killer whales are made up of the mother's immediate and extended family members? They may stay together as a family even after they're fully grown and can live anywhere from 50 to 80 years.¶Today, we saw a number of sea lions and otters frolicking in the water. It was quite peculiar to see one otter lying on its back; it had a stone on its belly and a scallop in its paw. We discovered afterwards that otters float on their backs while they crack open the seashell of their prey with a rock.¶You won't believe this - there's a pair of bald eagles nesting in Aunt Joyce and Uncle Ross's very own backyard. It's astounding to see the eagles swooping in at speeds of up to 160 kilometres per hour. They can spot fish from about 1.5 kilometres away! The term "eagle eyes" is no joke.¶Aunt Joyce doesn't mind the eagles hanging out in their fir trees, but she does get frustrated with the deer and rabbits that come on their grounds often. These sneaky vegetarians arrive after dusk, having already eaten their main meal in nearby fields, only to enjoy Aunt Joyce's roses and lilies for dessert. I guess they feel comfortable trespassing on the property, since there is no dog to frighten them off.¶Tomorrow, Uncle Ross is taking us on an excursion to Johnstone Strait, where he is confident that we will see a pod or two of orcas. Apparently in July and August, the number of whales in this area peaks due to the salmon passing through (one of their favourite foods). They naturally make this one of their main foraging territories. I'll give you more details when I get home.

Love,
Nicole

B. 1. F　2. O
   3. F　4. F
   5. F　6. O

C. 1. She saw a pod of approximately 20 orcas.
   2. She saw two bald eagles spot fish from a great distance.
   3. They were deer and rabbits that frequented Uncle Ross and Aunt Joyce's grounds.

D. 1. astounding　2. peculiar
   3. incredible　4. foraging
   5. swooping　6. dorsal
   7. frolicking　8. sneaky

a	t	o					[illegible]	y	b
a	e	r	o	a	t	n	o	w	e
s	q	o	b	d	o	r	s	a	l
e	h	i	k	c	t	n	n	s	m
l	k	n	t	i	s	i	e	t	f
m	i	n	o	k	w	e	a	o	r
a	n	e	r	f	o	h	k	u	o
e	c	g	e	r	o	n	y	n	t
m	r	o	i	o	p	v	i	d	y
p	e	c	u	l	i	a	r	i	a
e	d	f	t	i	n	s	d	n	r
t	i	o	r	c	g	e	v	g	p
e	b	r	e	k	v	b	t	e	u
n	l	a	b	i	i	a	p	b	y
b	e	g	i	n	c	t	e	r	p
g	a	i	p	g					
i	a	n	t	a					
v	n	g	t	y					

E. 1. P 2. A
3. P 4. P
5. A 6. A

F. A: A big fish was spotted by the bald eagle.
B: We were taken to the shore by Uncle Ross in his van.
C: Aunt Joyce prepared a hearty meal for us.

Mathematics

A. 1.
$$\begin{array}{r} 3.97 \\ \times \quad 5 \\ \hline 19.85 \end{array}$$
; $19.85

2.
$$\begin{array}{r} 2.57 \\ \times \quad 4 \\ \hline 10.28 \end{array}$$
; $10.28

3.
$$\begin{array}{r} 7.89 \\ \times \quad 7 \\ \hline 55.23 \end{array}$$
; $55.23

4.
$$\begin{array}{r} 9.15 \\ \times \quad 3 \\ \hline 27.45 \end{array}$$
; $27.45

5. *Total Cost of Juice*
$$\begin{array}{r} 4.99 \\ 2.87 \\ + \; 0.96 \\ \hline 8.82 \end{array}$$
$8.82

Total Amount of Juice
$$\begin{array}{r} 950 \\ 598 \\ + \; 250 \\ \hline 1798 \end{array}$$
1798 mL

B. Combo A: 3.59 + 1.50 + 1.98 – 1.88 = 5.19 ; 5.19
Combo B: 2.59 + 1.96 + 1.29 – 1.88 = 3.96 ; 3.96
Combo C: 3.69 + 1.42 + 2.09 – 1.88 = 5.32 ; 5.32
Combo D: 1.50 + 1.50 + 1.98 – 1.88 = 3.10 ; 3.10
Combo E: 2.59 + 1.96 + 2.09 –1.88 = 4.76 ; 4.76

C. 1. Spinner A: 90˚ ; 90˚ ; 90˚ ; 90˚
top ; yo-yo ; doll ; car
Spinner B: 120˚ ; 120˚ ; 120˚
top ; car ; doll

2a. $\frac{90}{360} = \frac{1}{4}$

b. 0

3. Spinner B

D.

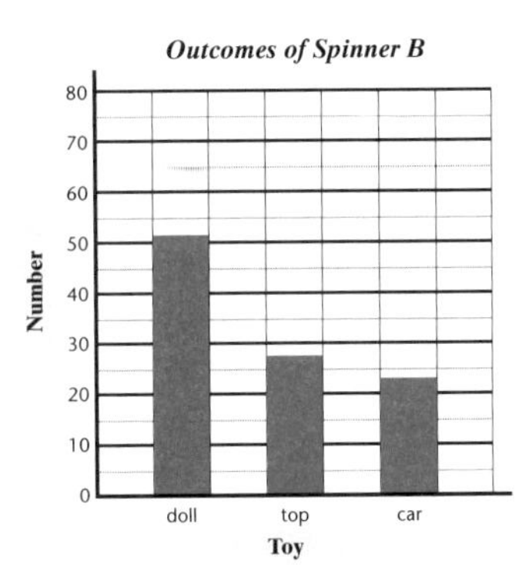

1. about $\frac{1}{2}$
2. No, the spinner should have landed on the doll as many times as it did on the top and the car. There is a $\frac{1}{3}$ chance of getting each item.
3. about 25 times

Science

A. Lever: G ; L ; greater
Pulley: L ; G ; greater
Inclined Plane: G ; L ; greater

B. First-class Lever: fulcrum ; A ; D
Second-class Lever: load ; C ; D
Third-class Lever: effort ; A ; D

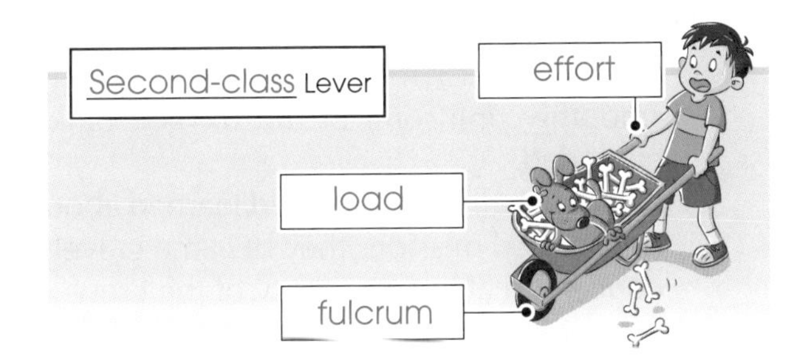

Social Studies

A. 1. Jewish ; worship ; pray
2. Mennonite ; plain ; horses
3. Muslim ; fasting ; public

B. C ; A ; D ; B

Week 5

English

B. 1. to explore the moon
2. James Lovell

3. Haise
4. Swigert
5. April 11, 1970
6. April 17, 1970
7. the Odyssey
8. Aquarius
9. An oxygen tank exploded.
10. Their spacecraft was losing oxygen, power, and its ability to navigate.
11. It was built for only two people and with enough supplies for only two days.
12. They used the stars.

C. 1. conserved 2. inconceivable
3. navigate 4. precise
5. transmitted

D. (Suggested answers)
disappear ; appearance
misconceive ; inconceivable
uneventful ; uneventfully
hopeful ; hopeless
unhappy ; happiness

E. Compound Sentence: B ; C
Complex Sentence: A ; D

F. (Suggested answers)
A: Since the navigation system on their spacecraft did not function properly, the astronauts had to rely on the stars for navigation.
B: The Apollo 13 mission was progressing smoothly until one of the oxygen tanks exploded.
C: As people all over the world learned about the aborted mission, they became gravely concerned about the safety of the crew.

Mathematics

A. 1. 250 ; 250 ; 250 ; 3
2. 275 ; 175 ; 225 ; 300

B. 25 hundredths ; 45 hundredths ; 0.45

A	A	A	A	A	A	A	A	A	A
A	A	A	A	A	A	A	A	A	A
A	A	A	A	A	A	A	A	A	A
M	M	M	M	M	M	M	M	M	M
M	M	M	M	M	M	M	M	M	M
M	M	M	M	M	Y	Y	Y	Y	Y
Y	Y	Y	Y	Y	Y	Y	Y	Y	Y
Y	Y	Y	Y	Y	Y	Y	Y	Y	Y
Y	Y	Y	Y	Y	Y	Y	Y	Y	Y
Y	Y	Y	Y	Y	Y	Y	Y	Y	Y

35 hundredths ; 0.2 ; 40 hundredths ; 0.4

T	T	T	T	T	O	O	O	O	O
O	O	O	O	O	O	O	O	O	O
O	O	O	O	O	O	O	O	O	O
O	O	O	O	O	O	O	O	O	O
N	N	N	N	N	N	N	N	N	N
N	N	N	N	N	N	N	N	N	N
Y	Y	Y	Y	Y	Y	Y	Y	Y	Y
Y	Y	Y	Y	Y	Y	Y	Y	Y	Y
Y	Y	Y	Y	Y	Y	Y	Y	Y	Y
Y	Y	Y	Y	Y	Y	Y	Y	Y	Y

C. (Suggested answers for "Coloured Part")

	Volume	Coloured Part
E	10 cm^3	$\frac{5}{10}$; $\frac{1}{2}$
L	7 cm^3	$\frac{4}{7}$; $\frac{8}{14}$
I	9 cm^3	$\frac{4}{9}$; $\frac{8}{18}$

	Volume	Coloured Part
T	7 cm^3	$\frac{2}{7}$; $\frac{4}{14}$
O	12 cm^3	$\frac{5}{12}$; $\frac{10}{24}$
N	15 cm^3	$\frac{6}{15}$; $\frac{12}{30}$
Y	7 cm^3	$\frac{5}{7}$; $\frac{10}{14}$

D. 1. 70° 2. 55°
3. 60° 4. 80°

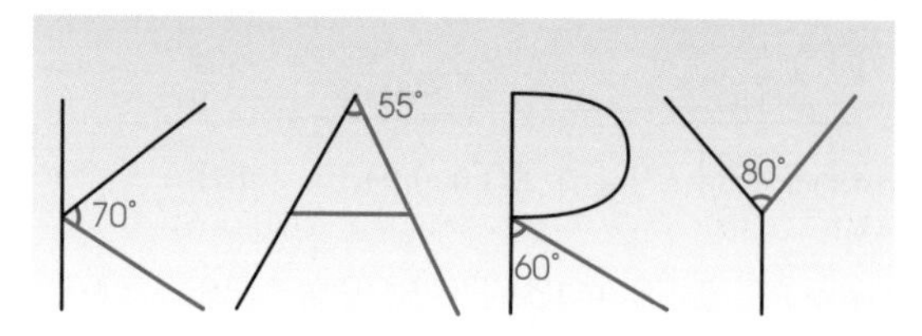

Science

A. Digestive System:
organ: stomach – gastric ; small intestine – 4.5 m ; rectum – large intestine
function: eat ; nutrients ; removed
Respiratory System:
organ: lungs – 3 ; 2
function: air ; oxygen ; carbon dioxide
Circulatory System:
organ: heart – fist
function: blood
Nervous System:
organ: brain – soft ; 1.5 kg
function: nerves ; body

Social Studies

A. 1. name 2. parents
3. needs 4. opinion
5. education 6. religion
7. play

B. A. health B. armed
C. minimum D. abuse
E. education F. increased
G. mines

The Canadian Charter of Rights and Freedoms: E
Federal Government: B ; D ; F
Provincial Government: A ; C ; G

Week 6

English

A. 1. F 2. T
3. T 4. F
5. F

B. (Individual questions)

C. (Individual writing)

D. 1. brave 2. ill
3. careful 4. vacation
5. found 6. strong
7. whisper 8. appear
9. flour 10. pause
11. mussel 12. plain
13. scene
Victoria Falls
14. Victoria Falls is a popular tourist attraction.
15. Victoria Falls is located in southern Africa.

Mathematics

A. 1. 0.9 km ; 1.8 km ; 3.1 km ; 3.7 km ; 4.9 km
2. 1.1 km ; 2.3 km ; 2.9 km ; 4.2 km ; 5.1 km
3. 8 minutes
4. 750 m

B. 1. B 2. C
3. B 4. A

C. 1. biscuits: 1210 ; 370 g
cookies: 450 g ; 395 g
popcorn: 650 g ; 250 g

2. $5\frac{1}{2}$

3. $97\frac{3}{4}$

4. $6\frac{1}{2}$

D.

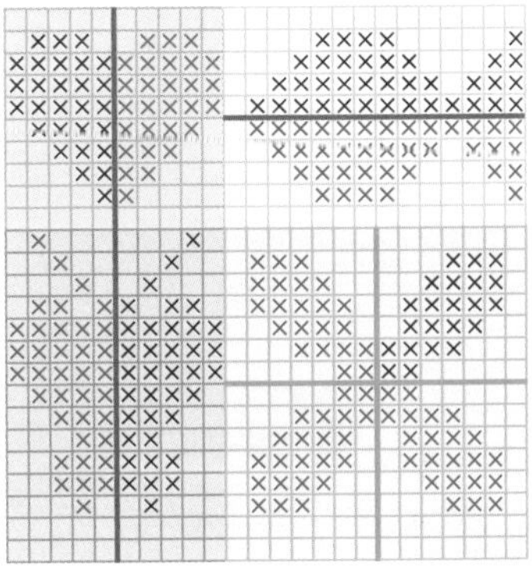

Science

A. 1. matter 2. space
3. volume 4. weight
5. scale

B. 1. viscosity
2. hardness
3. malleability
4. clarity
5. texture
6. solubility
7. lustre
8. honey: high ; translucent
knife: opaque ; shiny
chopping board: high ; smooth
sugar: high ; shiny

Social Studies

A. (Individual choice and answer)

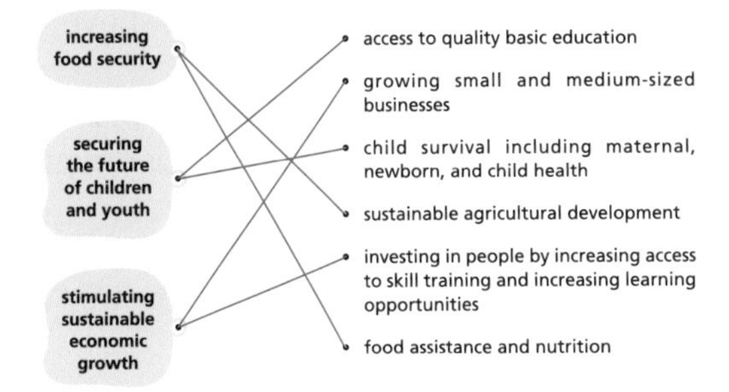

B. RCMP ; search ; medical ; relief
food ; treatment ; donations ; contributed

Week 7

English

B.

C. 1. "lovely" little brother Leo
2. tedious toddler tunes
3. offensively odoured outhouses
4. leeches latched onto my leg
5. exceptionally exciting experiences
(Individual writing)

D. 1. C 2. C
3. A

E. (Individual writing)

Mathematics

A. 1a. 250 trays b. 5 months
c. September
2a. 300 trays b. 1 month
c. September

B. 1. The new flavour was introduced in July because the sales of muffins have been increasing since July.
2. 600 trays of muffins will be sold in October.
3. The average number of trays of doughnuts sold per month was 400.
4. It opened in June because the sales of doughnuts have been decreasing since June.

C. 1. Regular: 0.64
Family: 0.60
Party: 0.54

2.

No. of Boxes (Regular-sized)	No. of Muffins	Cost
1	4	$2.56
2	8	$5.12
3	12	$7.68
4	16	$10.24
5	20	$12.80

3. 2.56 + 3.60 = 6.16
He should buy a regular-sized box and a family-sized box of muffins. It will cost $6.16.

4. 2.56 x 3 – 6.48 = 1.2
She saved $1.20.

D. Check: B, D
B: (15x5+15x10+10x5)x2=550 ; 550
D: (20x5+20x15+15x5)x2=950 ; 950

Science

A. 1. solid 2. gas
3. liquid 4. gas
5. liquid 6. solid
7. liquid 8. gas

B. 1. freezing ; taken away
melting ; added
2. condensation ; taken away
3. evaporation ; added
4a. sublimation
b. added

Social Studies

A. 1. greenhouse gas emissions
2. 1998
3. increasing
4. no

B. Introduction to Canada: unintentional ; North ; ships
Areas Affected: United States
Major Impact: mussels ; sinking ; aquatic
(Individual answer)